Anne Frank

The Diary of Anne Frank

Excerpts from Anne Frank: The Diary of a Young Girl

HOUGHTON MIFFLIN COMPANY BOSTON

Atlanta   Dallas   Geneva, Illinois   Palo Alto   Princeton   Toronto

Acknowledgments

The Diary of Anne Frank by Frances Goodrich and Albert Hackett. Copyright © 1954 as an unpublished work by Albert Hackett, Frances Goodrich Hackett and Otto Frank. Reprinted by permission of Random House, Inc.

Introduction by Eleanor Roosevelt and excerpts from *Anne Frank: The Diary of a Young Girl* by Anne Frank. Copyright © 1952 by Otto H. Frank. Reprinted by permission of Doubleday & Company, Inc. and Vallentine & Mitchell Company, Ltd.

"I Dream a World" by Langston Hughes. Reprinted by permission of Harold Ober Associates Incorporated. Copyright © 1945 by Langston Hughes.

Credits

Cover photography: AP/Wide World

Photography AP/Wide World: pp. 210, 211L.
        Bettman Newsphotos: p. 188.
        Fred Fehl: pp. 10, 116, 117.
        Magnum/Henri Cartier-Bresson: p. 211R.
        TIB / © Kuhn, Inc.: pp. 208–209.

Printed in the U.S.A.
ISBN: 0-395-45996-6
   DEFGHIJ-B-976543210/89

Can you imagine what it would be like to hide in an attic for two years, unable to make any sound during the day for fear of being discovered and losing your life? This is what Anne Frank and her family had to do. Because they were Jewish, they were in danger from the moment the Nazis gained control of Germany.

Led by Adolf Hitler, the Nazis believed themselves to be a "master race" whose enemies were Jewish people everywhere. Thus, when they invaded Holland, they rounded up all the Jewish people, put them into concentration camps, and then exterminated them in cruel and inhuman ways, often torturing them first. In all, the Nazis murdered twelve million people they believed to be inferior or to be political enemies. Six million of those murdered were Jewish.

The selections in this book represent one girl's experiences during those horrible times.

Table of Contents

Introduction

To escape the inhuman treatment of Jews inflicted by the Nazis during World War II, Anne Frank and her family went into hiding on July 9, 1942. Taking with them only the barest necessities, the Franks lived for two years, with four other friends, in the attic—called the "Secret Annex"—of a warehouse in Amsterdam.

In August 1944, the Frank family and their friends were discovered and carted off to different concentration camps where all of them except Mr. Frank died. He returned to Amsterdam and discovered the diary Anne had kept during their two years in hiding. This play is based on Anne's diary.

The Diary
of
Anne Frank

Dramatized by

FRANCES GOODRICH and ALBERT HACKETT

(Based upon the book ANNE FRANK: DIARY OF A YOUNG GIRL)

With a foreword by BROOKS ATKINSON

THE DIARY OF ANNE FRANK *was first presented by Kermit Bloomgarden at the Cort Theatre, New York City, on October 5, 1955, with the following cast:*

(IN ORDER OF APPEARANCE)

MR. FRANK	Joseph Schildkraut
MIEP	Gloria Jones
MRS. VAN DAAN	Dennie Moore
MR. VAN DAAN	Lou Jacobi
PETER VAN DAAN	David Levin
MRS. FRANK	Gusti Huber
MARGOT FRANK	Eva Rubinstein
ANNE FRANK	Susan Strasberg
MR. KRALER	Clinton Sundberg
MR. DUSSEL	Jack Gilford

Directed by Garson Kanin

Production designed by Boris Aronson

Costumes by Helene Pons

Lighting by Leland Watson

The guidance of Mr. Otto H. Frank, Dr. L. de Jong, Miss Lidia Winkle and The Netherlands State Institute for War Documentation, Amsterdam, is gratefully acknowledged.

The Time: During the years of World War II and immediately thereafter.

The Place: Amsterdam

There are two acts

ACT ONE

ACT ONE

Scene I

The scene remains the same throughout the play. It is the top floor of a warehouse and office building in Amsterdam, Holland. The sharply peaked roof of the building is outlined against a sea of other rooftops, stretching away into the distance. Nearby is the belfry of a church tower, the Westertoren, whose carillon rings out the hours. Occasionally faint sounds float up from below: the voices of children playing in the street, the tramp of marching feet, a boat whistle from the canal.

The three rooms of the top floor and a small attic space above are exposed to our view. The largest of the rooms is in the center, with two small rooms, slightly raised, on either side. On the right is a bathroom, out of sight. A narrow steep flight of stairs at the back leads up to the attic. The rooms are sparsely furnished with a few chairs, cots, a table or two. The windows are painted over, or covered with makeshift blackout curtains. In the main room there is a sink, a gas ring for cooking and a wood-burning stove for warmth.

The room on the left is hardly more than a closet. There is a skylight in the sloping ceiling. Directly under this room is a small steep stairwell, with steps leading down to a door. This is the only entrance from the building below. When the door is opened we see that it has been concealed on the outer side by a bookcase attached to it.

The curtain rises on an empty stage. It is late afternoon November, 1945.

The rooms are dusty, the curtains in rags. Chairs and tables are overturned.

The door at the foot of the small stairwell swings open. MR. FRANK *comes up the steps into view. He is a gentle, cultured European in his middle years. There is still a trace of a German accent in his speech.*

He stands looking slowly around, making a supreme effort at self-control. He is weak, ill. His clothes are threadbare.

After a second he drops his rucksack on the couch and moves slowly about. He opens the door to one of the smaller rooms, and then abruptly closes it again, turning away. He goes to the window at the back, looking off at the Westertoren as its carillon strikes the hour of six, then he moves restlessly on.

From the street below we hear the sound of a barrel organ and children's voices at play. There is a many-colored scarf hanging from a nail. MR. FRANK *takes it, putting it around his neck. As he starts back for his rucksack, his eye is caught by something lying on the floor. It is a woman's white glove. He holds it in his hand and suddenly all of his self-control is gone. He breaks down, crying.*

We hear footsteps on the stairs. MIEP GIES *comes up, looking for* MR. FRANK. MIEP *is a Dutch girl of about twenty-two. She wears a coat and hat, ready to go home. She is pregnant. Her attitude toward* MR. FRANK *is protective, compassionate.*

MIEP

Are you all right, Mr. Frank?

MR. FRANK

(*Quickly controlling himself*)

Yes, Miep, yes.

MIEP

Everyone in the office has gone home . . . It's after six. (*Then pleading*) Don't stay up here, Mr. Frank. What's the use of torturing yourself like this?

MR. FRANK

I've come to say good-bye . . . I'm leaving here, Miep.

MIEP

What do you mean? Where are you going? Where?

MR. FRANK

I don't know yet. I haven't decided.

MIEP

Mr. Frank, you can't leave here! This is your home! Amsterdam is your home. Your business is here, waiting for you . . . You're needed here . . . Now that the war is over, there are things that . . .

MR. FRANK

I can't stay in Amsterdam, Miep. It has too many memories for me. Everywhere there's something . . . the house we lived in . . . the school . . . that street organ playing out there . . . I'm not the person you used to know, Miep. I'm a bitter old man. (*Breaking off*) Forgive me. I shouldn't speak to you like this . . . after all that you did for us . . . the suffering . . .

MIEP

No. No. It wasn't suffering. You can't say we suffered.

(*As she speaks, she straightens a chair which is over-turned.*)

MR. FRANK

I know what you went through, you and Mr. Kraler. I'll remember it as long as I live. (*He gives one last look around*) Come, Miep.

(*He starts for the steps, then remembers his rucksack, going back to get it.*)

MIEP

(*Hurrying up to a cupboard*)

Mr. Frank, did you see? There are some of your papers here. (*She brings a bundle of papers to him*) We found them in a heap of rubbish on the floor after . . . after you left.

MR. FRANK

Burn them.

(*He opens his rucksack to put the glove in it.*)

MIEP

But, Mr. Frank, there are letters, notes . . .

MR. FRANK

Burn them. All of them.

MIEP

Burn *this?*

(*She hands him a paperbound notebook.*)

MR. FRANK

(*Quietly*)

Anne's diary. (*He opens the diary and begins to read*) "Monday, the sixth of July, nineteen forty-two." (*To* MIEP) Nineteen forty-two. Is it possible, Miep? . . . Only three years ago. (*As he continues his reading, he sits down on the couch*) "Dear Diary, since you and I are going to be great friends, I will start by telling you about myself. My name is Anne Frank. I am thirteen years old. I was born in Germany the twelfth of June, nineteen twenty-nine. As my family is Jewish, we emigrated to Holland when Hitler came to power."

(*As* MR. FRANK *reads on, another voice joins his, as if coming from the air. It is* ANNE'S VOICE.)

MR. FRANK AND ANNE

"My father started a business, importing spice and herbs. Things went well for us until nineteen forty. Then the war came, and the Dutch capitulation, followed by the arrival of the Germans. Then things got very bad for the Jews."

(MR. FRANK'S VOICE *dies out.* ANNE'S VOICE *continues alone. The lights dim slowly to darkness. The curtain falls on the scene.*)

ANNE'S VOICE

You could not do this and you could not do that. They forced Father out of his business. We had to wear yellow stars. I had to turn in my bike. I couldn't go to a Dutch school any more. I couldn't go to the movies, or ride in an automobile, or even on a streetcar, and a million other things. But somehow we children still managed to have fun. Yesterday Father told me we were going into hiding. Where, he wouldn't say. At five o'clock this morning Mother woke me and told me to hurry and get dressed. I was to put on as many clothes as I could. It would look too suspicious if we walked along carrying suitcases. It wasn't until we were on our way that I learned where we were going. Our hiding place was to be upstairs in the building where Father used to have his business. Three other people were coming in with us . . . the Van Daans and their son Peter . . . Father knew the Van Daans but we had never met them . . .

(*During the last lines the curtain rises on the scene. The lights dim on.* ANNE'S VOICE *fades out.*)

SCENE II

It is early morning, July, 1942. The rooms are bare, as before, but they are now clean and orderly.

MR. VAN DAAN, *a tall, portly man in his late forties, is in the main room, pacing up and down, nervously smoking a cigarette. His clothes and overcoat are expensive and well cut.*

MRS. VAN DAAN *sits on the couch, clutching her possessions, a hatbox, bags, etc. She is a pretty woman in her early forties. She wears a fur coat over her other clothes.*

PETER VAN DAAN *is standing at the window of the room on the right, looking down at the street below. He is a shy, awkward boy of sixteen. He wears a cap, a raincoat, and long Dutch trousers, like "plus fours."¹ At his feet is a black case, a carrier for his cat.*

The yellow Star of David² is conspicuous on all of their clothes.

MRS. VAN DAAN

(*Rising, nervous, excited*)
Something's happened to them! I know it!

MR. VAN DAAN

Now, Kerli!

MRS. VAN DAAN

Mr. Frank said they'd be here at seven o'clock. He said . . .

MR. VAN DAAN

They have two miles to walk. You can't expect . . .

---

¹*plus fours:* loose pants gathered below the knees.
²*Star of David:* The six-pointed star is a Jewish symbol. The Nazis required all Jews to display the star to make them immediately identifiable as Jews.

MRS. VAN DAAN

They've been picked up. That's what's happened. They've been taken . . .

(MR. VAN DAAN *indicates that he hears someone coming.*)

MR. VAN DAAN

You see?

(PETER *takes up his carrier and his schoolbag, etc., and goes into the main room as* MR. FRANK *comes up the stairwell from below.* MR. FRANK *looks much younger now. His movements are brisk, his manner confident. He wears an overcoat and carries his hat and a small cardboard box. He crosses to the* VAN DAANS, *shaking hands with each of them.*)

MR. FRANK

Mrs. Van Daan, Mr. Van Daan, Peter. (*Then, in explanation of their lateness*) There were too many of the Green Police[3] on the streets . . . we had to take the long way around.

(*Up the steps come* MARGOT FRANK, MRS. FRANK, MIEP (*not pregnant now*) *and* MR. KRALER. *All of them carry bags, packages, and so forth. The Star of David is conspicuous on all of the* FRANKS' *clothing.* MARGOT *is eighteen, beautiful, quiet, shy.* MRS. FRANK *is a young mother, gently bred, reserved. She, like* MR. FRANK, *has a slight German accent.* MR. KRALER *is a Dutchman, dependable, kindly.*

As MR. KRALER *and* MIEP *go upstage to put down their parcels,* MRS. FRANK *turns back to call* ANNE.)

---

[3]*Green Police:* Nazi police, their uniforms were green.

MRS. FRANK

Anne?

(ANNE *comes running up the stairs. She is thirteen, quick in her movements, interested in everything, mercurial in her emotions. She wears a cape, long wool socks and carries a schoolbag.*)

MR. FRANK

(*Introducing them*)

My wife, Edith. Mr. and Mrs. Van Daan (MRS. FRANK *hurries over, shaking hands with them*) . . . their son, Peter . . . my daughters, Margot and Anne.

(ANNE *gives a polite little curtsy as she shakes* MR. VAN DAAN's *hand. Then she immediately starts off on a tour of investigation of her new home, going upstairs to the attic room.*

MIEP *and* MR. KRALER *are putting the various things they have brought on the shelves.*)

MR. KRALER

I'm sorry there is still so much confusion.

MR. FRANK

Please. Don't think of it. After all, we'll have plenty of leisure to arrange everything ourselves.

MIEP

(*To* MRS. FRANK)

We put the stores of food you sent in here. Your drugs are here . . . soap, linen here.

MRS. FRANK

Thank you, Miep.

MIEP

I made up the beds . . . the way Mr. Frank and Mr. Kraler said. (*She starts out*) Forgive me. I have to hurry. I've got to go to the other side of town to get some ration books[4] for you.

MRS. VAN DAAN

Ration books? If they see our names on ration books, they'll know we're here.

MR. KRALER

There isn't anything . . .

MIEP

Don't worry. Your names won't be on them. (*As she hurries out*) I'll be up later.

} *Together*

MR. FRANK

Thank you, Miep.

MRS. FRANK

(*To* MR. KRALER)

It's illegal, then, the ration books? We've never done anything illegal.

MR. FRANK

We won't be living here exactly according to regulations.

(*As* MR. KRALER *reassures* MRS. FRANK, *he takes various small things, such as matches, soap, etc., from his pockets, handing them to her.*)

---

[4]*ration books:* books of coupons which allowed the bearer to buy a fixed amount of provisions or food.

MR. KRALER

This isn't the black market, Mrs. Frank. This is what we call the white market[5] . . . helping all of the hundreds and hundreds who are hiding out in Amsterdam.

(*The carillon is heard playing the quarter-hour before eight.* MR. KRALER *looks at his watch.* ANNE *stops at the window as she comes down the stairs.*)

ANNE

It's the Westertoren!

MR. KRALER

I must go. I must be out of here and downstairs in the office before the workmen get here. (*He starts for the stairs leading out*) Miep or I, or both of us, will be up each day to bring you food and news and find out what your needs are. Tomorrow I'll get you a better bolt for the door at the foot of the stairs. It needs a bolt that you can throw yourself and open only at our signal. (*To* MR. FRANK) Oh . . . You'll tell them about the noise?

MR. FRANK

I'll tell them.

MR. KRALER

Good-bye then for the moment. I'll come up again, after the workmen leave.

MR. FRANK

Good-bye, Mr. Kraler.

---

[5]*black market...white market:* black market goods were sold illegally, usually at a very high price. The goods the Franks were receiving (white market) were donated by people wishing to help the Jews.

MRS. FRANK

(*Shaking his hand*)
How can we thank you?
(*The others murmur their good-byes.*)

MR. KRALER

I never thought I'd live to see the day when a man like Mr. Frank would have to go into hiding. When you think—
(*He breaks off, going out.* MR. FRANK *follows him down the steps, bolting the door after him. In the interval before he returns,* PETER *goes over to* MARGOT, *shaking hands with her. As* MR. FRANK *comes back up the steps,* MRS. FRANK *questions him anxiously.*)

MRS. FRANK

What did he mean, about the noise?

MR. FRANK

First let us take off some of these clothes.
(*They all start to take off garment after garment. On each of their coats, sweaters, blouses, suits, dresses, is another yellow Star of David.* MR. *and* MRS. FRANK *are underdressed quite simply. The others wear several things, sweaters, extra dresses, bathrobes, aprons, nightgowns, etc.*)

MR. VAN DAAN

It's a wonder we weren't arrested, walking along the streets . . . Petronella with a fur coat in July . . . and that cat of Peter's crying all the way.

ANNE
(*As she is removing a pair of panties*)

A cat?

MRS. FRANK
(*Shocked*)

Anne, please!

ANNE

It's all right. I've got on three more.
(*She pulls off two more. Finally, as they have all removed their surplus clothes, they look to* MR. FRANK, *waiting for him to speak.*)

MR. FRANK

Now. About the noise. While the men are in the building below, we must have complete quiet. Every sound can be heard down there, not only in the workrooms, but in the offices too. The men come at about eight-thirty, and leave at about five-thirty. So, to be perfectly safe, from eight in the morning until six in the evening we must move only when it is necessary, and then in stockinged feet. We must not speak above a whisper. We must not run any water. We cannot use the sink, or even, forgive me, the w.c. The pipes go down through the workrooms. It would be heard. No trash . . . (MR. FRANK *stops abruptly as he hears the sound of marching feet from the street below. Everyone is motionless, paralyzed with fear.* MR. FRANK *goes quietly into the room on the right to look down out of the window.* ANNE *runs after him, peering out with him. The tramping feet pass without stopping. The tension is relieved.* MR. FRANK, *followed by* ANNE, *returns to the main room and resumes his in-*

structions to the group) . . . No trash must ever be thrown out which might reveal that someone is living up here . . . not even a potato paring. We must burn everything in the stove at night. This is the way we must live until it is over, if we are to survive.

(*There is silence for a second.*)

MRS. FRANK

Until it is over.

MR. FRANK

(*Reassuringly*)

After six we can move about . . . we can talk and laugh and have our supper and read and play games . . . just as we would at home. (*He looks at his watch*) And now I think it would be wise if we all went to our rooms, and were settled before eight o'clock. Mrs. Van Daan, you and your husband will be upstairs. I regret that there's no place up there for Peter. But he will be here, near us. This will be our common room, where we'll meet to talk and eat and read, like one family.

MR. VAN DAAN

And where do you and Mrs. Frank sleep?

MR. FRANK

This room is also our bedroom.

MRS. VAN DAAN

That isn't right. We'll sleep here and you take the room upstairs.

Together

MR. VAN DAAN

It's your place.

MR. FRANK

Please. I've thought this out for weeks. It's the best arrangement. The only arrangement.

MRS. VAN DAAN

(*To* MR. FRANK)

Never, never can we thank you. (*Then to* MRS. FRANK) I don't know what would have happened to us, if it hadn't been for Mr. Frank.

MR. FRANK

You don't know how your husband helped me when I came to this country . . . knowing no one . . . not able to speak the language. I can never repay him for that. (*Going to* VAN DAAN) May I help you with your things?

MR. VAN DAAN

No. No. (*To* MRS. VAN DAAN) Come along, *liefje.*[6]

MRS. VAN DAAN

You'll be all right, Peter? You're not afraid?

PETER

(*Embarrassed*)

Please, Mother.

(*They start up the stairs to the attic room above.* MR. FRANK *turns to* MRS. FRANK.)

MR. FRANK

You too must have some rest, Edith. You didn't close your eyes last night. Nor you, Margot.

---

[6] *liefje:* Dutch for "little love."

ANNE

I slept, Father. Wasn't that funny? I knew it was the last night in my own bed, and yet I slept soundly.

MR. FRANK

I'm glad, Anne. Now you'll be able to help me straighten things in here. (*To* MRS. FRANK *and* MARGOT) Come with me ... You and Margot rest in this room for the time being.

(*He picks up their clothes, starting for the room on the right.*)

MRS. FRANK

You're sure ... ? I could help ... And Anne hasn't had her milk ...

MR. FRANK

I'll give it to her. (*To* ANNE *and* PETER) Anne, Peter ... it's best that you take off your shoes now, before you forget.

(*He leads the way to the room, followed by* MARGOT.)

MRS. FRANK

You're sure you're not tired, Anne?

ANNE

I feel fine. I'm going to help Father.

MRS. FRANK

Peter, I'm glad you are to be with us.

PETER

Yes, Mrs. Frank.

(MRS. FRANK *goes to join* MR. FRANK *and* MARGOT.)

(*During the following scene* MR. FRANK *helps* MARGOT *and* MRS. FRANK *to hang up their clothes. Then he persuades them both to lie down and rest. The* VAN DAANS *in their room above settle themselves. In the main room* ANNE *and* PETER *remove their shoes.* PETER *takes his cat out of the carrier.*)

ANNE

What's your cat's name?

PETER

Mouschi.

ANNE

Mouschi! Mouschi! Mouschi! (*She picks up the cat, walking away with it. To* PETER) I love cats. I have one . . . a darling little cat. But they made me leave her behind. I left some food and a note for the neighbors to take care of her . . . I'm going to miss her terribly. What is yours? A him or a her?

PETER

He's a tom. He doesn't like strangers.
(*He takes the cat from her, putting it back in its carrier.*)

ANNE
(*Unabashed*)
Then I'll have to stop being a stranger, won't I? Is he fixed?

PETER
(*Startled*)

Huh?

ANNE

Did you have him fixed?

PETER

No.

ANNE

Oh, you ought to have him fixed—to keep him from—you know, fighting. Where did you go to school?

PETER

Jewish Secondary.

ANNE

But that's where Margot and I go! I never saw you around.

PETER

I used to see you . . . sometimes . . .

ANNE

You did?

PETER

. . . in the school yard. You were always in the middle of a bunch of kids.

(*He takes a penknife from his pocket.*)

ANNE

Why didn't you ever come over?

PETER

I'm sort of a lone wolf.

(*He starts to rip off his Star of David.*)

ANNE

What are you doing?

PETER

Taking it off.

ANNE

But you can't do that. They'll arrest you if you go out without your star.

(*He tosses his knife on the table.*)

PETER

Who's going out?

ANNE

Why, of course! You're right! Of course we don't need them any more. (*She picks up his knife and starts to take her star off*) I wonder what our friends will think when we don't show up today?

PETER

I didn't have any dates with anyone.

ANNE

Oh, I did. I had a date with Jopie to go and play ping-pong at her house. Do you know Jopie de Waal?

PETER

No.

ANNE

Jopie's my best friend. I wonder what she'll think when she telephones and there's no answer? . . . Probably she'll go over to the house . . . I wonder what she'll think . . . we left every-thing as if we'd suddenly been called away . . . breakfast dishes in the sink . . . beds not made . . . (*As she pulls off her star, the cloth underneath shows clearly the color and form of the star*) Look! It's still there! (PETER *goes over to the stove with his star*) What're you going to do with yours?

PETER

Burn it.

ANNE

(*She starts to throw hers in, and cannot*)
It's funny, I can't throw mine away. I don't know why.

PETER

You can't throw . . . ? Something they branded you with . . . ? That they made you wear so they could spit on you?

ANNE

I know. I know. But after all, it *is* the Star of David, isn't it?
(*In the bedroom, right,* MARGOT *and* MRS. FRANK *are lying down.* MR. FRANK *starts quietly out.*)

PETER

Maybe it's different for a girl.
(MR. FRANK *comes into the main room.*)

MR. FRANK

Forgive me, Peter. Now let me see. We must find a bed for your cat. (*He goes to a cupboard*) I'm glad you brought your cat. Anne was feeling so badly about hers. (*Getting a used small washtub*) Here we are. Will it be comfortable in that?

PETER
(*Gathering up his things*)
Thanks.

MR. FRANK
(*Opening the door of the room on the left*)
And here is your room. But I warn you, Peter, you can't grow any more. Not an inch, or you'll have to sleep with your feet out of the skylight. Are you hungry?

PETER
No.

MR. FRANK
We have some bread and butter.

PETER
No, thank you.

MR. FRANK
You can have it for luncheon then. And tonight we will have a real supper . . . our first supper together.

PETER
Thanks. Thanks.
(*He goes into his room. During the following scene he arranges his possessions in his new room.*)

MR. FRANK
That's a nice boy, Peter.

ANNE

He's awfully shy, isn't he?

MR. FRANK

You'll like him, I know.

ANNE

I certainly hope so, since he's the only boy I'm likely to see for months and months.

(MR. FRANK *sits down, taking off his shoes.*)

MR. FRANK

Anneke, there's a box there. Will you open it?

(*He indicates a carton on the couch.* ANNE *brings it to the center table. In the street below there is the sound of children playing.*)

ANNE

(*As she opens the carton*)

You know the way I'm going to think of it here? I'm going to think of it as a boarding house. A very peculiar summer boarding house, like the one that we—(*She breaks off as she pulls out some photographs*) Father! My movie stars! I was wondering where they were! I was looking for them this morning . . . and Queen Wilhelmina! How wonderful!

MR. FRANK

There's something more. Go on. Look further.

(*He goes over to the sink, pouring a glass of milk from a thermos bottle.*)

ANNE

(*Pulling out a pasteboard-bound book*)
A diary! (*She throws her arms around her father*) I've never had a diary. And I've always longed for one. (*She looks around the room*) Pencil, pencil, pencil, pencil. (*She starts down the stairs*) I'm going down to the office to get a pencil.

MR. FRANK

Anne! No!
(*He goes after her, catching her by the arm and pulling her back.*)

ANNE

(*Startled*)
But there's no one in the building now.

MR. FRANK

It doesn't matter. I don't want you ever to go beyond that door.

ANNE

(*Sobered*)
Never ... ? Not even at nighttime, when everyone is gone? Or on Sundays? Can't I go down to listen to the radio?

MR. FRANK

Never. I am sorry, Anneke. It isn't safe. No, you must never go beyond that door.
(*For the first time* ANNE *realizes what "going into hiding" means.*)

ANNE

I see.

MR. FRANK

It'll be hard, I know. But always remember this, Anneke. There are no walls, there are no bolts, no locks that anyone can put on your mind. Miep will bring us books. We will read history, poetry, mythology. (*He gives her the glass of milk*) Here's your milk. (*With his arm about her, they go over to the couch, sitting down side by side*) As a matter of fact, between us, Anne, being here has certain advantages for you. For instance, you remember the battle you had with your mother the other day on the subject of overshoes? You said you'd rather die than wear overshoes? But in the end you had to wear them? Well now, you see, for as long as we are here you will never have to wear overshoes! Isn't that good? And the coat that you inherited from Margot, you won't have to wear that any more. And the piano! You won't have to practice on the piano. I tell you, this is going to be a fine life for you!

> (ANNE's *panic is gone.* PETER *appears in the doorway of his room, with a saucer in his hand. He is carrying his cat.*)

PETER

I . . . I . . . I thought I'd better get some water for Mouschi before . . .

MR. FRANK

Of course.

> (*As he starts toward the sink the carillon begins to chime the hour of eight. He tiptoes to the window at the back*

and looks down at the street below. He turns to PETER, *indicating in pantomime that it is too late.* PETER *starts back for his room. He steps on a creaking board. The three of them are frozen for a minute in fear. As* PETER *starts away again,* ANNE *tiptoes over to him and pours some of the milk from her glass into the saucer for the cat.* PETER *squats on the floor, putting the milk before the cat.* MR. FRANK *gives* ANNE *his fountain pen, and then goes into the room at the right. For a second* ANNE *watches the cat, then she goes over to the center table, and opens her diary.*

In the room at the right, MRS. FRANK *has sat up quickly at the sound of the carillon.* MR. FRANK *comes in and sits down beside her on the settee, his arm comfortingly around her.*

Upstairs, in the attic room, MR. *and* MRS. VAN DAAN *have hung their clothes in the closet and are now seated on the iron bed.* MRS. VAN DAAN *leans back exhausted.* MR. VAN DAAN *fans her with a newspaper.*

ANNE *starts to write in her diary. The lights dim out, the curtain falls.*

In the darkness ANNE'S VOICE *comes to us again, faintly at first, and then with growing strength.*)

ANNE'S VOICE

I expect I should be describing what it feels like to go into hiding. But I really don't know yet myself. I only know it's funny never to be able to go outdoors . . . never to breathe fresh air . . . never to run and shout and jump. It's the silence in the nights that frightens me most. Every time I hear a creak in the house, or a step on the street outside, I'm sure they're coming for us. The days aren't so bad. At least we know that Miep and Mr. Kraler are down there below us in the office. Our protectors, we call them. I asked Father what would happen to them if the Nazis found out they were hiding us. Pim[7] said that they would suffer the same fate that we would . . . Imagine! They know this, and yet when they come up here, they're always cheerful and gay as if there were nothing in the world to bother them . . . Friday, the twenty-first of August, nineteen forty-two. Today I'm going to tell you our general news. Mother is unbearable. She insists on treating me like a baby, which I loathe. Otherwise things are going better. The weather is . . .

(*As* ANNE'S VOICE *is fading out, the curtain rises on the scene.*)

[7]*Pim:* Anne's nickname for her father.

Scene III

It is a little after six o'clock in the evening, two months later.
MARGOT *is in the bedroom at the right, studying.* MR. VAN
DAAN *is lying down in the attic room above.*

The rest of the "family" is in the main room. ANNE *and* PETER
*sit opposite each other at the center table, where they have been
doing their lessons.* MRS. FRANK *is on the couch.* MRS. VAN DAAN
*is seated with her fur coat, on which she has been sewing, in her
lap. None of them are wearing their shoes.*

Their eyes are on MR. FRANK, *waiting for him to give them
the signal which will release them from their day-long quiet.*
MR. FRANK, *his shoes in his hand, stands looking down out of
the window at the back, watching to be sure that all of the
workmen have left the building below.*

After a few seconds of motionless silence, MR. FRANK *turns
from the window.*

MR. FRANK

(*Quietly, to the group*)
It's safe now. The last workman has left.
(*There is an immediate stir of relief.*)

ANNE

(*Her pent-up energy explodes*)
WHEE!

MRS. FRANK

(*Startled, amused*)

Anne!

MRS. VAN DAAN

I'm first for the w.c.

(*She hurries off to the bathroom.* MRS. FRANK *puts on her shoes and starts up to the sink to prepare supper.* ANNE *sneaks* PETER'S *shoes from under the table and hides them behind her back.* MR. FRANK *goes in to* MARGOT'S *room.*)

MR. FRANK

(*To* MARGOT)

Six o'clock. School's over.

(MARGOT *gets up, stretching.* MR. FRANK *sits down to put on his shoes. In the main room* PETER *tries to find his.*)

PETER

(*To* ANNE)

Have you seen my shoes?

ANNE

(*Innocently*)

Your shoes?

PETER

You've taken them, haven't you?

ANNE

I don't know what you're talking about.

PETER

You're going to be sorry!

ANNE

Am I?

(PETER *goes after her.* ANNE, *with his shoes in her hand, runs from him, dodging behind her mother.*)

MRS. FRANK

(*Protesting*)

Anne, dear!

PETER

Wait till I get you!

ANNE

I'm waiting! (PETER *makes a lunge for her. They both fall to the floor.* PETER *pins her down, wrestling with her to get the shoes*) Don't! Don't! Peter, stop it. Ouch!

MRS. FRANK

Anne! . . . Peter!

(*Suddenly* PETER *becomes self-conscious. He grabs his shoes roughly and starts for his room.*)

ANNE

(*Following him*)

Peter, where are you going? Come dance with me.

PETER

I tell you I don't know how.

ANNE

I'll teach you.

PETER

I'm going to give Mouschi his dinner.

ANNE

Can I watch?

PETER

He doesn't like people around while he eats.

ANNE

Peter, please.

PETER

No!

(*He goes into his room.* ANNE *slams his door after him.*)

MRS. FRANK

Anne, dear, I think you shouldn't play like that with Peter. It's not dignified.

ANNE

Who cares if it's dignified? I don't want to be dignified.

(MR. FRANK *and* MARGOT *come from the room on the right.* MARGOT *goes to help her mother.* MR. FRANK *starts for the center table to correct* MARGOT's *school papers.*)

MRS. FRANK

(*To* ANNE)

You complain that I don't treat you like a grownup. But when I do, you resent it.

ANNE

I only want some fun . . . someone to laugh and clown with
. . . After you've sat still all day and hardly moved, you've got
to have some fun. I don't know what's the matter with that
boy.

MR. FRANK

He isn't used to girls. Give him a little time.

ANNE

Time? Isn't two months time? I could cry. (*Catching hold of*
MARGOT) Come on, Margot . . . dance with me. Come on,
please.

MARGOT

I have to help with supper.

ANNE

You know we're going to forget how to dance . . . When we
get out we won't remember a thing.
(*She starts to sing and dance by herself.* MR. FRANK *takes
her in his arms, waltzing with her.* MRS. VAN DAAN *comes
in from the bathroom.*)

MRS. VAN DAAN

Next? (*She looks around as she starts putting on her shoes*)
Where's Peter?

ANNE
(*As they are dancing*)
Where would he be!

MRS. VAN DAAN

He hasn't finished his lessons, has he? His father'll kill him if he catches him in there with that cat and his work not done. (MR. FRANK *and* ANNE *finish their dance. They bow to each other with extravagant formality*) Anne, get him out of there, will you?

ANNE
(*At* PETER'S *door*)

Peter? Peter?

PETER
(*Opening the door a crack*)

What is it?

ANNE

Your mother says to come out.

PETER

I'm giving Mouschi his dinner.

MRS. VAN DAAN

You know what your father says.
(*She sits on the couch, sewing on the lining of her fur coat.*)

PETER

For heaven's sake, I haven't even looked at him since lunch.

MRS. VAN DAAN

I'm just telling you, that's all.

ANNE

I'll feed him.

PETER

I don't want you in there.

MRS. VAN DAAN

Peter!

PETER

(*To* ANNE)

Then give him his dinner and come right out, you hear?

(*He comes back to the table.* ANNE *shuts the door of* PETER's *room after her and disappears behind the curtain covering his closet.*)

MRS. VAN DAAN

(*To* PETER)

Now is that any way to talk to your little girl friend?

PETER

Mother . . . for heaven's sake . . . will you please stop saying that?

MRS. VAN DAAN

Look at him blush! Look at him!

PETER

Please! I'm not . . . anyway . . . let me alone, will you?

MRS. VAN DAAN

He acts like it was something to be ashamed of. It's nothing to be ashamed of, to have a little girl friend.

PETER

You're crazy. She's only thirteen.

MRS. VAN DAAN

So what? And you're sixteen. Just perfect. Your father's ten years older than I am. (*To* MR. FRANK) I warn you, Mr. Frank, if this war lasts much longer, we're going to be related and then . . .

MR. FRANK

Mazeltov![8]

MRS. FRANK

(*Deliberately changing the conversation*)
I wonder where Miep is. She's usually so prompt.
(*Suddenly everything else is forgotten as they hear the sound of an automobile coming to a screeching stop in the street below. They are tense, motionless in their terror. The car starts away. A wave of relief sweeps over them. They pick up their occupations again.* ANNE *flings open the door of* PETER's *room, making a dramatic entrance. She is dressed in* PETER's *clothes.* PETER *looks at her in fury. The others are amused.*)

ANNE

Good evening, everyone. Forgive me if I don't stay. (*She jumps up on a chair*)I have a friend waiting for me in there. My friend Tom. Tom Cat. Some people say that we look alike. But Tom has the most beautiful whiskers, and I have only a little fuzz. I am hoping . . . in time . . .

---

[8]*Mazeltov:* Yiddish for "congratulations."

PETER

All right, Mrs. Quack Quack!

ANNE

(*Outraged—jumping down*)

Peter!

PETER

I heard about you ... How you talked so much in class they called you Mrs. Quack Quack. How Mr. Smitter made you write a composition ... " 'Quack, quack,' said Mrs. Quack Quack."

ANNE

Well, go on. Tell them the rest. How it was so good he read it out loud to the class and then read it to all his other classes!

PETER

Quack! Quack! Quack ... Quack ... Quack ...

(ANNE *pulls off the coat and trousers*)

ANNE

You are the most intolerable, insufferable boy I've ever met!

(*She throws the clothes down the stairwell.* PETER *goes down after them.*)

PETER

Quack, quack, quack!

MRS. VAN DAAN

(*To* ANNE)

That's right, Anneke! Give it to him!

ANNE

With all the boys in the world . . . Why I had to get locked up with one like you! . . .

PETER

Quack, quack, quack, and from now on stay out of my room!
(*As* PETER *passes her,* ANNE *puts out her foot, tripping him. He picks himself up, and goes on into his room.*)

MRS. FRANK
(*Quietly*)
Anne, dear . . . your hair. (*She feels* ANNE's *forehead*) You're warm. Are you feeling all right?

ANNE

Please, Mother.
(*She goes over to the center table, slipping into her shoes.*)

MRS. FRANK
(*Following her*)
You haven't a fever, have you?

ANNE
(*Pulling away*)
No. No.

MRS. FRANK

You know we can't call a doctor here, ever. There's only one thing to do . . . watch carefully. Prevent an illness before it comes. Let me see your tongue.

ANNE

Mother, this is perfectly absurd.

MRS. FRANK

Anne, dear, don't be such a baby. Let me see your tongue. (*As* ANNE *refuses,* MRS. FRANK *appeals to* MR. FRANK) Otto . . . ?

MR. FRANK

You hear your mother, Anne.
(ANNE *flicks out her tongue for a second, then turns away.*)

MRS. FRANK

Come on—open up! (*As* ANNE *opens her mouth very wide*) You seem all right . . . but perhaps an aspirin . . .

MRS. VAN DAAN

For heaven's sake, don't give that child any pills. I waited for fifteen minutes this morning for her to come out of the w.c.

ANNE

I was washing my hair!

MR. FRANK

I think there's nothing the matter with our Anne that a ride on her bike, or a visit with her friend Jopie de Waal wouldn't cure. Isn't that so, Anne?
(MR. VAN DAAN *comes down into the room. From outside we hear faint sounds of bombers going over and a burst of ack-ack.*)

MR. VAN DAAN

Miep not come yet?

MRS. VAN DAAN

The workmen just left, a little while ago.

MR. VAN DAAN

What's for dinner tonight?

MRS. VAN DAAN

Beans.

MR. VAN DAAN

Not again!

MRS. VAN DAAN

Poor Putti! I know. But what can we do? That's all that Miep brought us.

(MR. VAN DAAN *starts to pace, his hands behind his back.* ANNE *follows behind him, imitating him.*)

ANNE

We are now in what is known as the "bean cycle." Beans boiled, beans en casserole, beans with strings, beans without strings . . .

(PETER *has come out of his room. He slides into his place at the table, becoming immediately absorbed in his studies.*)

MR. VAN DAAN
(*To* PETER)

I saw you . . . in there, playing with your cat.

MRS. VAN DAAN

He just went in for a second, putting his coat away. He's been out here all the time, doing his lessons.

MR. FRANK

(*Looking up from the papers*)
Anne, you got an excellent in your history paper today . . . and very good in Latin.

ANNE

(*Sitting beside him*)
How about algebra?

MR. FRANK

I'll have to make a confession. Up until now I've managed to stay ahead of you in algebra. Today you caught up with me. We'll leave it to Margot to correct.

ANNE

Isn't algebra *vile*, Pim!

MR. FRANK

Vile!

MARGOT

(*To* MR. FRANK)
How did I do?

ANNE

(*Getting up*)
Excellent, excellent, excellent, excellent!

MR. FRANK

(*To* MARGOT)

You should have used the subjunctive here . . .

MARGOT

Should I? . . . I thought . . . look here . . . I didn't use it here . . .

(*The two become absorbed in the papers.*)

ANNE

Mrs. Van Daan, may I try on your coat?

MRS. FRANK

No, Anne.

MRS. VAN DAAN

(*Giving it to* ANNE)

It's all right . . . but careful with it. (ANNE *puts it on and struts with it*) My father gave me that the year before he died. He always bought the best that money could buy.

ANNE

Mrs. Van Daan, did you have a lot of boy friends before you were married?

MRS. FRANK

Anne, that's a personal question. It's not courteous to ask personal questions.

MRS. VAN DAAN

Oh I don't mind. (*To* ANNE) Our house was always swarming with boys. When I was a girl we had . . .

MR. VAN DAAN

Oh, God. Not again!

MRS. VAN DAAN

(*Good-humored*)

Shut up! (*Without a pause, to* ANNE. MR. VAN DAAN *mimics*
MRS. VAN DAAN, *speaking the first few words in unison with her*)
One summer we had a big house in Hilversum. The boys came
buzzing round like bees around a jam pot. And when I was
sixteen! . . . We were wearing our skirts very short those days
and I had good-looking legs. (*She pulls up her skirt, going to*
MR. FRANK) I still have 'em. I may not be as pretty as I used to
be, but I still have my legs. How about it, Mr. Frank?

MR. VAN DAAN

All right. All right. We see them.

MRS. VAN DAAN

I'm not asking you. I'm asking Mr. Frank.

PETER

Mother, for heaven's sake.

MRS. VAN DAAN

Oh, I embarrass you, do I? Well, I just hope the girl you
marry has as good. (*Then to* ANNE) My father used to worry
about me, with so many boys hanging round. He told me, if
any if them gets fresh, you say to him . . . "Remember, Mr.
So-and-So, remember I'm a lady."

ANNE

"Remember, Mr. So-and-So, remember I'm a lady."
(*She gives* MRS. VAN DAAN *her coat.*)

MR. VAN DAAN

Look at you, talking that way in front of her! Don't you know she puts it all down in that diary?

MRS. VAN DAAN

So, if she does? I'm only telling the truth!
(ANNE *stretches out, putting her ear to the floor, listening to what is going on below. The sound of the bombers fades away.*)

MRS. FRANK

(*Setting the table*)
Would you mind, Peter, if I moved you over to the couch?

ANNE

(*Listening*)
Miep must have the radio on.
(PETER *picks up his papers, going over to the couch beside* MRS. VAN DAAN.)

MR. VAN DAAN

(*Accusingly, to* PETER)
Haven't you finished yet?

PETER

No.

MR. VAN DAAN

You ought to be ashamed of yourself.

PETER

All right. All right. I'm a dunce. I'm a hopeless case. Why do I go on?

MRS. VAN DAAN

You're not hopeless. Don't talk that way. It's just that you haven't anyone to help you, like the girls have. (*To* MR. FRANK) Maybe you could help him, Mr. Frank?

MR. FRANK

I'm sure that his father . . . ?

MR. VAN DAAN

Not me. I can't do anything with him. He won't listen to me. You go ahead . . . if you want.

MR. FRANK

(*Going to* PETER)

What about it, Peter? Shall we make our school coeducational?

MRS. VAN DAAN

(*Kissing* MR. FRANK)

You're an angel, Mr. Frank. An angel. I don't know why I didn't meet you before I met that one there. Here, sit down, Mr. Frank . . . (*She forces him down on the couch beside* PETER) Now, Peter, you listen to Mr. Frank.

MR. FRANK

It might be better for us to go into Peter's room.
(PETER *jumps up eagerly, leading the way.*)

MRS. VAN DAAN

That's right. You go in there, Peter. You listen to Mr. Frank.
Mr. Frank is a highly educated man.
(*As* MR. FRANK *is about to follow* PETER *into his room,*
MRS. FRANK *stops him and wipes the lipstick from his
lips. Then she closes the door after them.*)

ANNE

(*On the floor, listening*)
Shh! I can hear a man's voice talking.

MR. VAN DAAN

(*To* ANNE)
Isn't it bad enough here without your sprawling all over the
place?
(ANNE *sits up.*)

MRS. VAN DAAN

(*To* MR. VAN DAAN)
If you didn't smoke so much, you wouldn't be so bad-tem-
pered.

MR. VAN DAAN

Am I smoking? Do you see me smoking?

MRS. VAN DAAN

Don't tell me you've used up all those cigarettes.

MR. VAN DAAN

One package. Miep only brought me one package.

MRS. VAN DAAN

It's a filthy habit anyway. It's a good time to break yourself.

MR. VAN DAAN

Oh, stop it, please.

MRS. VAN DAAN

You're smoking up all our money. You know that, don't you?

MR. VAN DAAN

Will you shut up? (*During this,* MRS. FRANK *and* MARGOT *have studiously kept their eyes down. But* ANNE, *seated on the floor, has been following the discussion interestedly.* MR. VAN DAAN *turns to see her staring up at him*) And what are you staring at?

ANNE

I never heard grownups quarrel before. I thought only children quarreled.

MR. VAN DAAN

This isn't a quarrel! It's a discussion. And I never heard children so rude before.

ANNE

(*Rising, indignantly*)

I, rude!

MR. VAN DAAN

Yes!

MRS. FRANK

(*Quickly*)

Anne, will you get me my knitting? (ANNE *goes to get it*) I must remember, when Miep comes, to ask her to bring me some more wool.

MARGOT

(*Going to her room*)

I need some hairpins and some soap. I made a list.
(*She goes into her bedroom to get the list.*)

MRS. FRANK

(*To* ANNE)

Have you some library books for Miep when she comes?

ANNE

It's a wonder that Miep has a life of her own, the way we make her run errands for us. Please, Miep, get me some starch. Please take my hair out and have it cut. Tell me all the latest news, Miep. (*She goes over, kneeling on the couch beside* MRS. VAN DAAN) Did you know she was engaged? His name is Dirk, and Miep's afraid the Nazis will ship him off to Germany to work in one of their war plants. That's what they're doing with some of the young Dutchmen . . . they pick them up off the streets—

MR. VAN DAAN

(*Interrupting*)

Don't you ever get tired of talking? Suppose you try keeping still for five minutes. Just five minutes.

(He starts to pace again. Again ANNE *follows him, mimicking him.* MRS. FRANK *jumps up and takes her by the arm up to the sink, and gives her a glass of milk.)*

MRS. FRANK

Come here, Anne. It's time for your glass of milk.

MR. VAN DAAN

Talk, talk, talk. I never heard such a child. Where is my . . . ? Every evening it's the same, talk, talk, talk. *(He looks around)* Where is my . . . ?

MRS. VAN DAAN

What're you looking for?

MR. VAN DAAN

My pipe. Have you seen my pipe?

MRS. VAN DAAN

What good's a pipe? You haven't got any tobacco.

MR. VAN DAAN

At least I'll have something to hold in my mouth! *(Opening* MARGOT's *bedroom door)* Margot, have you seen my pipe?

MARGOT

It was on the table last night.
*(*ANNE *puts her glass of milk on the table and picks up his pipe, hiding it behind her back.)*

MR. VAN DAAN

I know. I know. Anne, did you see my pipe? . . . Anne!

MRS. FRANK

Anne, Mr. Van Daan is speaking to you.

ANNE

Am I allowed to talk now?

MR. VAN DAAN

You're the most aggravating . . . The trouble with you is, you've been spoiled. What you need is a good old-fashioned spanking.

ANNE

(*Mimicking* MRS. VAN DAAN)

"Remember, Mr. So-and-So, remember I'm a lady."

(*She thrusts the pipe into his mouth, then picks up her glass of milk.*)

MR. VAN DAAN

(*Restraining himself with difficulty*)

Why aren't you nice and quiet like your sister Margot? Why do you have to show off all the time? Let me give you a little advice, young lady. Men don't like that kind of thing in a girl. You know that? A man likes a girl who'll listen to him once in a while . . . a domestic girl, who'll keep her house shining for her husband . . . who loves to cook and sew and . . .

ANNE

I'd cut my throat first! I'd open my veins! I'm going to be remarkable! I'm going to Paris . . .

MR. VAN DAAN

(*Scoffingly*)

Paris!

ANNE

. . . to study music and art.

MR. VAN DAAN

Yeah! Yeah!

ANNE

I'm going to be a famous dancer or singer . . . or something wonderful.

(*She makes a wide gesture, spilling the glass of milk on the fur coat in* MRS. VAN DAAN's *lap.* MARGOT *rushes quickly over with a towel.* ANNE *tries to brush the milk off with her skirt.*)

MRS. VAN DAAN

Now look what you've done . . . you clumsy little fool! My beautiful fur coat my father gave me . . .

ANNE

I'm so sorry.

MRS. VAN DAAN

What do you care? It isn't yours . . . So go on, ruin it! Do you know what that coat cost? Do you? And now look at it! Look at it!

ANNE

I'm very, very sorry.

MRS. VAN DAAN

I could kill you for this. I could just kill you!

(MRS. VAN DAAN *goes up the stairs, clutching the coat.* MR. VAN DAAN *starts after her.*)

MR. VAN DAAN

Petronella . . . *liefje! Liefje!* . . . Come back . . . the supper . . . come back!

MRS. FRANK

Anne, you must not behave in that way.

ANNE

It was an accident. Anyone can have an accident.

MRS. FRANK

I don't mean that. I mean the answering back. You must not answer back. They are our guests. We must always show the greatest courtesy to them. We're all living under terrible tension. (*She stops as* MARGOT *indicates that* VAN DAAN *can hear. When he is gone, she continues*) That's why we must control ourselves . . . You don't hear Margot getting into arguments with them, do you? Watch Margot. She's always courteous with them. Never familiar. She keeps her distance. And they respect her for it. Try to be like Margot.

ANNE

And have them walk all over me, the way they do her? No, thanks!

MRS. FRANK

I'm not afraid that anyone is going to walk all over you, Anne. I'm afraid for other people, that you'll walk on them. I don't know what happens to you, Anne. You are wild, self-willed. If I had ever talked to my mother as you talk to me . . .

ANNE

Things have changed. People aren't like that any more. "Yes, Mother." "No, Mother." "Anything you say, Mother." I've got to fight things out for myself! Make something of myself!

MRS. FRANK

It isn't necessary to fight to do it. Margot doesn't fight, and isn't she . . . ?

ANNE

(Violently rebellious)

Margot! Margot! Margot! That's all I hear from everyone . . . how wonderful Margot is . . . "Why aren't you like Margot?"

MARGOT

(Protesting)

Oh, come on, Anne, don't be so . . .

ANNE

(Paying no attention)

Everything she does is right, and everything I do is wrong! I'm the goat around here! . . . You're all against me! . . . And you worst of all!

(*She rushes off into her room and throws herself down on the settee, stifling her sobs.* MRS. FRANK *sighs and starts toward the stove.*)

MRS. FRANK

(*To* MARGOT)

Let's put the soup on the stove . . . if there's anyone who cares to eat. Margot, will you take the bread out? (MARGOT *gets the bread from the cupboard*) I don't know how we can go on living this way . . . I can't say a word to Anne . . . she flies at me . . .

MARGOT

You know Anne. In half an hour she'll be out here, laughing and joking.

MRS. FRANK

And . . . (*She makes a motion upwards, indicating the* VAN DAANS) . . . I told your father it wouldn't work . . . but no . . . no . . . he had to ask them, he said . . . he owed it to him, he said. Well, he knows now that I was right! These quarrels! . . . This bickering!

MARGOT

(*With a warning look*)

Shush. Shush.

(*The buzzer for the door sounds.* MRS. FRANK *gasps, startled.*)

MRS. FRANK

Every time I hear that sound, my heart stops!

MARGOT

(*Starting for* PETER's *door*)

It's Miep. (*She knocks at the door*) Father?

(MR. FRANK *comes quickly from* PETER's *room.*)

MR. FRANK

Thank you, Margot. (*As he goes down the steps to open the outer door*) Has everyone his list?

MARGOT

I'll get my books. (*Giving her mother a list*) Here's your list. (MARGOT *goes into her and* ANNE's *bedroom on the right.* ANNE *sits up, hiding her tears, as* MARGOT *comes in*) Miep's here.

(MARGOT *picks up her books and goes back.* ANNE *hurries over to the mirror, smoothing her hair.*)

MR. VAN DAAN

(*Coming down the stairs*)

Is it Miep?

MARGOT

Yes. Father's gone down to let her in.

MR. VAN DAAN

At last I'll have some cigarettes!

MRS. FRANK

(*To* MR. VAN DAAN)

I can't tell you how unhappy I am about Mrs. Van Daan's coat. Anne should never have touched it.

MR. VAN DAAN

She'll be all right.

MRS. FRANK

Is there anything I can do?

MR. VAN DAAN

Don't worry.
> (*He turns to meet* MIEP. *But it is not* MIEP *who comes up the steps. It is* MR. KRALER, *followed by* MR. FRANK. *Their faces are grave.* ANNE *comes from the bedroom.* PETER *comes from his room.*)

MRS. FRANK

Mr. Kraler!

MR. VAN DAAN

How are you, Mr. Kraler?

MARGOT

This is a surprise.

MRS. FRANK

When Mr. Kraler comes, the sun begins to shine.

MR. VAN DAAN

Miep is coming?

MR. KRALER

Not tonight.
> (KRALER *goes to* MARGOT *and* MRS. FRANK *and* ANNE, *shaking hands with them.*)

MRS. FRANK

Wouldn't you like a cup of coffee? . . . Or, better still, will you have supper with us?

MR. FRANK

Mr. Kraler has something to talk over with us. Something has happened, he says, which demands an immediate decision.

MRS. FRANK

(*Fearful*)

What is it?

> (MR. KRALER *sits down on the couch. As he talks he takes bread, cabbages, milk, etc., from his briefcase, giving them to* MARGOT *and* ANNE *to put away.*)

MR. KRALER

Usually, when I come up here, I try to bring you some bit of good news. What's the use of telling you the bad news when there's nothing that you can do about it? But today something has happened . . . Dirk . . . Miep's Dirk, you know, came to me just now. He tells me that he has a Jewish friend living near him. A dentist. He says he's in trouble. He begged me, could I do anything for this man? Could I find him a hiding place? . . . So I've come to you . . . I know it's a terrible thing to ask of you, living as you are, but would you take him in with you?

MR. FRANK

Of course we will.

MR. KRALER

(Rising)

It'll be just for a night or two . . . until I find some other place. This happened so suddenly that I didn't know where to turn.

MR. FRANK

Where is he?

MR. KRALER

Downstairs in the office.

MR. FRANK

Good. Bring him up.

MR. KRALER

His name is Dussel . . . Jan Dussel.

MR. FRANK

Dussel . . . I think I know him.

MR. KRALER

I'll get him.

(*He goes quickly down the steps and out.* MR. FRANK *suddenly becomes conscious of the others.*)

MR. FRANK

Forgive me. I spoke without consulting you. But I knew you'd feel as I do.

MR. VAN DAAN

There's no reason for you to consult anyone. This is your place. You have a right to do exactly as you please. The only thing I feel . . . there's so little food as it is . . . and to take in another person . . .

(PETER *turns away, ashamed of his father*.)

MR. FRANK

We can stretch the food a little. It's only for a few days.

MR. VAN DAAN

You want to make a bet?

MRS. FRANK

I think it's fine to have him. But, Otto, where are you going to put him? Where?

PETER

He can have my bed. I can sleep on the floor. I wouldn't mind.

MR. FRANK

That's good of you, Peter. But your room's too small . . . even for *you*.

ANNE

I have a much better idea. I'll come in here with you and Mother, and Margot can take Peter's room and Peter can go in our room with Mr. Dussel.

MARGOT

That's right. We could do that.

MR. FRANK

No, Margot. You mustn't sleep in that room . . . neither you nor Anne. Mouschi has caught some rats in there. Peter's brave. He doesn't mind.

ANNE

Then how about *this?* I'll come in here with you and Mother, and Mr. Dussel can have my bed.

MRS. FRANK

No. No. *No!* Margot will come in here with us and he can have her bed. It's the only way. Margot, bring your things in here. Help her, Anne.

(MARGOT *hurries into her room to get her things.*)

ANNE

(*To her mother*)

Why Margot? Why can't I come in here?

MRS. FRANK

Because it wouldn't be proper for Margot to sleep with a . . . Please, Anne. Don't argue. Please.

(ANNE *starts slowly away.*)

MR. FRANK

(*To* ANNE)

You don't mind sharing your room with Mr. Dussel, do you, Anne?

ANNE

No. No, of course not.

MR. FRANK

Good. (ANNE *goes off into her bedroom, helping* MARGOT. MR. FRANK *starts to search in the cupboards*) Where's the cognac?

MRS. FRANK

It's there. But, Otto, I was saving it in case of illness.

MR. FRANK

I think we couldn't find a better time to use it. Peter, will you get five glasses for me?

(PETER *goes for the glasses.* MARGOT *comes out of her bedroom, carrying her possessions, which she hangs behind a curtain in the main room.* MR. FRANK *finds the cognac and pours it into the five glasses that* PETER *brings him.* MR. VAN DAAN *stands looking on sourly.* MRS. VAN DAAN *comes downstairs and looks around at all the bustle.*)

MRS. VAN DAAN

What's happening? What's going on?

MR. VAN DAAN

Someone's moving in with us.

MRS. VAN DAAN

In here? You're joking.

MARGOT

It's only for a night or two . . . until Mr. Kraler finds him another place.

MR. VAN DAAN

Yeah! Yeah!

(MR. FRANK *hurries over as* MR. KRALER *and* DUSSEL *come up.* DUSSEL *is a man in his late fifties, meticulous, finicky . . . bewildered now. He wears a raincoat. He carries a briefcase, stuffed full, and a small medicine case.*)

MR. FRANK

Come in, Mr. Dussel.

MR. KRALER

This is Mr. Frank.

DUSSEL

Mr. Otto Frank?

MR. FRANK

Yes. Let me take your things. (*He takes the hat and briefcase, but* DUSSEL *clings to his medicine case*) This is my wife Edith . . . Mr. and Mrs. Van Daan . . . their son, Peter . . . and my daughters, Margot and Anne.

(DUSSEL *shakes hands with everyone.*)

MR. KRALER

Thank you, Mr. Frank. Thank you all. Mr. Dussel, I leave you in good hands. Oh . . . Dirk's coat.

(DUSSEL *hurriedly takes off the raincoat, giving it to* MR. KRALER. *Underneath is his white dentist's jacket, with a yellow Star of David on it.*)

DUSSEL

(*To* MR. KRALER)

What can I say to thank you . . . ?

MRS. FRANK

(*To* DUSSEL)

Mr. Kraler and Miep . . . They're our life line. Without them we couldn't live.

MR. KRALER

Please. Please. You make us seem very heroic. It isn't that at all. We simply don't like the Nazis. (*To* MR. FRANK, *who offers him a drink*) No, thanks. (*Then going on*) We don't like their methods. We don't like . . .

MR. FRANK

(*Smiling*)

I know. I know. "No one's going to tell us Dutchmen what to do with our damn Jews!"

MR. KRALER

(*To* DUSSEL)

Pay no attention to Mr. Frank. I'll be up tomorrow to see that they're treating you right. (*To* MR. FRANK) Don't trouble to come down again. Peter will bolt the door after me, won't you, Peter?

PETER

Yes, sir.

MR. FRANK

Thank you, Peter. I'll do it.

MR. KRALER

Good night. Good night.

GROUP

Good night, Mr. Kraler.

We'll see you tomorrow, etc., etc.

(MR. KRALER *goes out with* MR. FRANK. MRS. FRANK *gives each one of the* "grownups" *a glass of cognac.*)

MRS. FRANK

Please, Mr. Dussel, sit down.

(MR. DUSSEL *sinks into a chair.* MRS. FRANK *gives him a glass of cognac.*)

DUSSEL

I'm dreaming. I know it. I can't believe my eyes. Mr. Otto Frank here! (*To* MRS. FRANK) You're not in Switzerland then? A woman told me . . . She said she'd gone to your house . . . the door was open, everything was in disorder, dishes in the sink. She said she found a piece of paper in the wastebasket with an address scribbled on it . . . an address in Zurich. She said you must have escaped to Zurich.

ANNE

Father put that there purposely . . . just so people would think that very thing!

DUSSEL

And you've been *here* all the time?

MRS. FRANK

All the time . . . ever since July.

(ANNE *speaks to her father as he comes back.*)

ANNE

It worked, Pim . . . the address you left! Mr. Dussel says that people believe we escaped to Switzerland.

MR. FRANK

I'm glad. . . . And now let's have a little drink to welcome Mr. Dussel. (*Before they can drink,* MR. DUSSEL *bolts his drink.* MR. FRANK *smiles and raises his glass*) To Mr. Dussel. Welcome. We're very honored to have you with us.

MRS. FRANK

To Mr. Dussel, welcome.
(*The* VAN DAANS *murmur a welcome. The "grownups" drink.*)

MRS. VAN DAAN

Um. That was good.

MR. VAN DAAN

Did Mr. Kraler warn you that you won't get much to eat here? You can imagine . . . three ration books among the seven of us . . . and now you make eight.
(PETER *walks away, humiliated. Outside a street organ is heard dimly.*)

DUSSEL

(*Rising*)

Mr. Van Daan, you don't realize what is happening outside that you should warn me of a thing like that. You don't realize what's going on . . . (*As* MR. VAN DAAN *starts his characteristic pacing,* DUSSEL *turns to speak to the others*) Right here in Amsterdam every day hundreds of Jews disappear . . . They surround a block and search house by house. Children come home from school to find their parents gone. Hundreds are being de-

ported . . . people that you and I know . . . the Hallensteins
. . . the Wessels . . .

MRS. FRANK

(*In tears*)

Oh, no. No!

DUSSEL

They get their call-up notice . . . come to the Jewish theatre
on such and such a day and hour . . . bring only what you can
carry in a rucksack. And if you refuse the call-up notice, then
they come and drag you from your home and ship you off to
Mauthausen. The death camp!

MRS. FRANK

We didn't know that things had got so much worse.

DUSSEL

Forgive me for speaking so.

ANNE

(*Coming to* DUSSEL)

Do you know the de Waals? . . . What's become of them?
Their daughter Jopie and I are in the same class. Jopie's my best
friend.

DUSSEL

They are gone.

ANNE

Gone?

DUSSEL

With all the others.

ANNE

Oh, no. Not Jopie!
(*She turns away, in tears.* MRS. FRANK *motions to* MARGOT *to comfort her.* MARGOT *goes to* ANNE, *putting her arms comfortingly around her.*)

MRS. VAN DAAN

There were some people called Wagner. They lived near us . . . ?

MR. FRANK

(*Interrupting, with a glance at* ANNE)
I think we should put this off until later. We all have many questions we want to ask . . . But I'm sure that Mr. Dussel would like to get settled before supper.

DUSSEL

Thank you. I would. I brought very little with me.

MR. FRANK

(*Giving him his hat and briefcase*)
I'm sorry we can't give you a room alone. But I hope you won't be too uncomfortable. We've had to make strict rules here . . . a schedule of hours . . . We'll tell you after supper. Anne, would you like to take Mr. Dussel to his room?

ANNE

(*Controlling her tears*)
If you'll come with me, Mr. Dussel?
(*She starts for her room.*)

DUSSEL

(*Shaking hands with each in turn*)

Forgive me if I haven't really expressed my gratitude to all of you. This has been such a shock to me. I'd always thought of myself as Dutch. I was born in Holland. My father was born in Holland, and my grandfather. And now . . . after all these years . . . (*He breaks off*) If you'll excuse me.

(DUSSEL *gives a little bow and hurries off after* ANNE. MR. FRANK *and the others are subdued.*)

ANNE

(*Turning on the light*)

Well, here we are.

(DUSSEL *looks around the room. In the main room* MARGOT *speaks to her mother.*)

MARGOT

The news sounds pretty bad, doesn't it? It's so different from what Mr. Kraler tells us. Mr. Kraler says things are improving.

MR. VAN DAAN

I like it better the way Kraler tells it.

(*They resume their occupations, quietly.* PETER *goes off into his room. In* ANNE'S *room,* ANNE *turns to* DUSSEL.)

ANNE

You're going to share the room with me.

DUSSEL

I'm a man who's always lived alone. I haven't had to adjust myself to others. I hope you'll bear with me until I learn.

ANNE

Let me help you. (*She takes his briefcase*) Do you always live all alone? Have you no family at all?

DUSSEL

No one.
(*He opens his medicine case and spreads his bottles on the dressing table.*)

ANNE

How dreadful. You must be terribly lonely.

DUSSEL

I'm used to it.

ANNE

I don't think I could ever get used to it. Didn't you even have a pet? A cat, or a dog?

DUSSEL

I have an allergy for fur-bearing animals. They give me asthma.

ANNE

Oh, dear. Peter has a cat.

DUSSEL

Here? He has it here?

ANNE

Yes. But we hardly ever see it. He keeps it in his room all the time. I'm sure it will be all right.

DUSSEL

Let us hope so.

(*He takes some pills to fortify himself.*)

ANNE

That's Margot's bed, where you're going to sleep. I sleep on the sofa there. (*Indicating the clothes hooks on the wall*) We cleared these off for your things. (*She goes over to the window*) The best part about this room . . . you can look down and see a bit of the street and the canal. There's a houseboat . . . you can see the end of it . . . a bargeman lives there with his family . . . They have a baby and he's just beginning to walk and I'm so afraid he's going to fall into the canal some day. I watch him. . . .

DUSSEL

(*Interrupting*)

Your father spoke of a schedule.

ANNE

(*Coming away from the window*)

Oh, yes. It's mostly about the times we have to be quiet. And times for the w.c. You can use it now if you like.

DUSSEL

(*Stiffly*)

No, thank you.

ANNE

I suppose you think it's awful, my talking about a thing like that. But you don't know how important it can get to be, especially when you're frightened . . . About this room, the way Margot and I did . . . she had it to herself in the afternoons for studying, reading . . . lessons, you know . . . and I took the mornings. Would that be all right with you?

DUSSEL

I'm not at my best in the morning.

ANNE

You stay here in the mornings then. I'll take the room in the afternoons.

DUSSEL

Tell me, when you're in here, what happens to me? Where am I spending my time? In there, with all the people?

ANNE

Yes.

DUSSEL

I see. I see.

ANNE

We have supper at half past six.

DUSSEL

(*Going over to the sofa*)

Then, if you don't mind . . . I like to lie down quietly for ten minutes before eating. I find it helps the digestion.

ANNE

Of course. I hope I'm not going to be too much of a bother to you. I seem to be able to get everyone's back up.

(DUSSEL *lies down on the sofa, curled up, his back to her.*)

DUSSEL

I always get along very well with children. My patients all bring their children to me, because they know I get on well with them. So don't you worry about that.

(ANNE *leans over him, taking his hand and shaking it gratefully.*)

ANNE

Thank you. Thank you, Mr. Dussel.

(*The lights dim to darkness. The curtain falls on the scene.* ANNE'S VOICE *comes to us faintly at first, and then with increasing power.*)

ANNE'S VOICE

. . . And yesterday I finished Cissy Van Marxvelt's latest book. I think she is a first-class writer. I shall definitely let my children read her. Monday the twenty-first of September, nineteen forty-two. Mr. Dussel and I had another battle yesterday. Yes, Mr. Dussel! According to him, nothing, I repeat . . . nothing, is right about me . . . my appearance, my character, my manners. While he was going on at me I thought . . . sometime I'll give you such a smack that you'll fly right up to the ceiling! Why is it that every grownup thinks he knows the way to bring up children? Particularly the grownups that never had any. I keep wishing that Peter was a girl instead of a boy. Then

I would have someone to talk to. Margot's a darling, but she takes everything too seriously. To pause for a moment on the subject of Mrs. Van Daan. I must tell you that her attempts to flirt with father are getting her nowhere. Pim, thank goodness, won't play.

> (*As she is saying the last lines, the curtain rises on the darkened scene.* ANNE'S VOICE *fades out.*)

Scene IV

It is the middle of the night, several months later. The stage is dark except for a little light which comes through the skylight in PETER'S *room.*

Everyone is in bed. MR. *and* MRS. FRANK *lie on the couch in the main room, which has been pulled out to serve as a make-shift double bed.*

MARGOT *is sleeping on a mattress on the floor in the main room, behind a curtain stretched across for privacy. The others are all in their accustomed rooms.*

From outside we hear two drunken soldiers singing "Lili Marlene." A girl's high giggle is heard. The sound of running feet is heard coming closer and then fading in the distance. Throughout the scene there is the distant sound of airplanes passing overhead.

A match suddenly flares up in the attic. We dimly see MR. VAN DAAN. *He is getting his bearings. He comes quickly down the stairs, and goes to the cupboard where the food is stored. Again the match flares up, and is as quickly blown out. The dim figure is seen to steal back up the stairs.*

There is quiet for a second or two, broken only by the sound of airplanes, and running feet on the street below.

Suddenly, out of the silence and the dark, we hear ANNE *scream.*

ANNE

(*Screaming*)

No! No! Don't . . . don't take me!

(*She moans, tossing and crying in her sleep. The other people wake, terrified.* DUSSEL *sits up in bed, furious.*)

DUSSEL

Shush! Anne! Anne, for God's sake, shush!

ANNE

(*Still in her nightmare*)

Save me! Save me!

(*She screams and screams.* DUSSEL *gets out of bed, going over to her, trying to wake her.*)

DUSSEL

For God's sake! Quiet! Quiet! You want someone to hear?

(*In the main room* MRS. FRANK *grabs a shawl and pulls it around her. She rushes in to* ANNE, *taking her in her arms.* MR. FRANK *hurriedly gets up, putting on his overcoat.* MARGOT *sits up, terrified.* PETER's *light goes on in his room.*)

MRS. FRANK

(*To* ANNE, *in her room*)

Hush, darling, hush. It's all right. It's all right. (*Over her shoulder to* DUSSEL) Will you be kind enough to turn on the light, Mr. Dussel? (*Back to* ANNE) It's nothing, my darling. It was just a dream.

(DUSSEL *turns on the light in the bedroom.* MRS. FRANK *holds* ANNE *in her arms. Gradually* ANNE *comes out of her nightmare, still trembling with horror.* MR. FRANK *comes into the room, and goes quickly to the window, looking out to be sure that no one outside has heard* ANNE'S *screams.* MRS. FRANK *holds* ANNE, *talking softly to her. In the main room* MARGOT *stands on a chair, turning on the center hanging lamp. A light goes on in the* VAN DAANS' *room overhead.* PETER *puts his robe on, coming out of his room.*)

DUSSEL

(*To* MRS. FRANK, *blowing his nose*)

Something must be done about that child, Mrs. Frank. Yelling like that! Who knows but there's somebody on the streets? She's endangering all our lives.

MRS. FRANK

Anne, darling.

DUSSEL

Every night she twists and turns. I don't sleep. I spend half my night shushing her. And now it's nightmares!

(MARGOT *comes to the door of* ANNE'S *room, followed by* PETER. MR. FRANK *goes to them, indicating that every-thing is all right.* PETER *takes* MARGOT *back.*)

MRS. FRANK

(*To* ANNE)

You're here, safe, you see? Nothing has happened. (*To* DUSSEL) Please, Mr. Dussel, go back to bed. She'll be herself in a minute or two. Won't you, Anne?

DUSSEL

(*Picking up a book and a pillow*)

Thank you, but I'm going to the w.c. The one place where there's peace!

(*He stalks out.* MR. VAN DAAN, *in underwear and trousers, comes down the stairs.*)

MR. VAN DAAN

(*To* DUSSEL)

What is it? What happened?

DUSSEL

A nightmare. She was having a nightmare!

MR. VAN DAAN

I thought someone was murdering her.

DUSSEL

Unfortunately, no.

(*He goes into the bathroom.* MR. VAN DAAN *goes back up the stairs.* MR. FRANK, *in the main room, sends* PETER *back to his own bedroom.*)

MR. FRANK

Thank you, Peter. Go back to bed.

(PETER *goes back to his room.* MR. FRANK *follows him, turning out the light and looking out the window. Then he goes back to the main room, and gets up on a chair, turning out the center hanging lamp.*)

MRS. FRANK

(*To* ANNE)

Would you like some water? (ANNE *shakes her head*) Was it a very bad dream? Perhaps if you told me . . . ?

ANNE

I'd rather not talk about it.

MRS. FRANK

Poor darling. Try to sleep then. I'll sit right here beside you until you fall asleep.

(*She brings a stool over, sitting there.*)

ANNE

You don't have to.

MRS. FRANK

But I'd like to stay with you . . . very much. Really.

ANNE

I'd rather you didn't.

MRS. FRANK

Good night, then. (*She leans down to kiss* ANNE. ANNE *throws her arm up over her face, turning away.* MRS. FRANK, *hiding her hurt, kisses* ANNE's *arm*) You'll be all right? There's nothing that you want?

ANNE

Will you please ask Father to come.

MRS. FRANK

(*After a second*)

Of course, Anne dear. (*She hurries out into the other room.*
MR. FRANK *comes to her as she comes in*) Sie verlangt nach Dir![9]

MR. FRANK

(*Sensing her hurt*)

Edith, *Liebe, schau* . . .[10]

MRS. FRANK

*Es macht nichts! Ich danke dem lieben Herrgott, dass sie sich
wenigstens an Dich wendet, wenn sie Trost braucht! Geh
hinein, Otto, sie ist ganz hysterisch vor Angst.*[11] (*As* MR. FRANK
hesitates) *Geh zu ihr.*[12] (*He looks at her for a second and then
goes to get a cup of water for* ANNE. MRS. FRANK *sinks down on
the bed, her face in her hands, trying to keep from sobbing
aloud.* MARGOT *comes over to her, putting her arms around her*)
She wants nothing of me. She pulled away when I leaned down
to kiss her.

MARGOT

It's a phase . . . You heard Father . . . Most girls go
through it . . . they turn to their fathers at this age . . . they
give all their love to their fathers.

MRS. FRANK

You weren't like this. You didn't shut me out.

MARGOT

She'll get over it . . .

(*She smooths the bed for* MRS. FRANK *and sits beside her
a moment as* MRS. FRANK *lies down. In* ANNE's *room* MR.

---

[9]*Sie verlangt nach Dir!:* "She's asking to see you."

[10]*Liebe, schau…:* "My Dear, look…"

[11]*Es macht…Angst:* "It doesn't matter. I just thank the dear Lord that when
she needs consolation she will at least turn to you. Go, Otto, she is hysterical
with fear."

[12]*Geh zu ihr:* "Go to her."

FRANK *comes in, sitting down by* ANNE. ANNE *flings her arms around him, clinging to him. In the distance we hear the sound of ack-ack.*)

ANNE

Oh, Pim. I dreamed that they came to get us! The Green Police! They broke down the door and grabbed me and started to drag me out the way they did Jopie.

MR. FRANK

I want you to take this pill.

ANNE

What is it?

MR. FRANK

Something to quiet you.
(*She takes it and drinks the water. In the main room* MARGOT *turns out the light and goes back to her bed.*)

MR. FRANK

(*To* ANNE)
Do you want me to read to you for a while?

ANNE

No. Just sit with me for a minute. Was I awful? Did I yell terribly loud? Do you think anyone outside could have heard?

MR. FRANK

No. No. Lie quietly now. Try to sleep.

ANNE

I'm a terrible coward. I'm so disappointed in myself. I think I've conquered my fear . . . I think I'm really grown-up . . . and then something happens . . . and I run to you like a baby . . . I love you, Father. I don't love anyone but you.

MR. FRANK

(*Reproachfully*)

Anneke!

ANNE

It's true. I've been thinking about it for a long time. You're the only one I love.

MR. FRANK

It's fine to hear you tell me that you love me. But I'd be happier if you said you loved your mother as well . . . She needs your help so much . . . your love . . .

ANNE

We have nothing in common. She doesn't understand me. Whenever I try to explain my views on life to her she asks me if I'm constipated.

MR. FRANK

You hurt her very much just now. She's crying. She's in there crying.

ANNE

I can't help it. I only told the truth. I didn't want her here . . . (*Then, with sudden change*) Oh, Pim, I was horrible, wasn't I? And the worst of it is, I can stand off and look at myself doing it and know it's cruel and yet I can't stop doing it. What's the matter with me? Tell me. Don't say it's just a phase! Help me.

MR. FRANK

There is so little that we parents can do to help our children. We can only try to set a good example . . . point the way. The rest you must do yourself. You must build your own character.

ANNE

I'm trying. Really I am. Every night I think back over all of the things I did that day that were wrong . . . like putting the wet mop in Mr. Dussel's bed . . . and this thing now with Mother. I say to myself, that was wrong. I make up my mind, I'm never going to do that again. Never! Of course I may do something worse . . . but at least I'll never do *that* again! . . . I have a nicer side, Father . . . a sweeter, nicer side. But I'm scared to show it. I'm afraid that people are going to laugh at me if I'm serious. So the mean Anne comes to the outside and the good Anne stays on the inside, and I keep on trying to switch them around and have the good Anne outside and the bad Anne inside and be what I'd like to be . . . and might be . . . if only . . . only . . .

(*She is asleep.* MR. FRANK *watches her for a moment and then turns off the light, and starts out. The lights dim out. The curtain falls on the scene.* ANNE's VOICE *is heard dimly at first, and then with growing strength.*)

ANNE's VOICE

. . . The air raids are getting worse. They come over day and night. The noise is terrifying. Pim says it should be music to our ears. The more planes, the sooner will come the end of the war. Mrs. Van Daan pretends to be a fatalist. What will be, will be. But when the planes come over, who is the most frightened? No one else but Petronella! . . . Monday, the ninth of November, nineteen forty-two. Wonderful news! The Allies have landed in Africa. Pim says that we can look for an early finish to the war. Just for fun he asked each of us what was the first thing we wanted to do when we got out of here. Mrs. Van Daan longs to be home with her own things, her needle-point chairs, the Beckstein piano her father gave her . . . the best that money could buy. Peter would like to go to a movie. Mr. Dussel wants to get back to his dentist's drill. He's afraid he is losing his touch. For myself, there are so many things . . . to ride a bike again . . . to laugh till my belly aches . . . to have new clothes from the skin out . . . to have a hot tub filled to overflowing and wallow in it for hours . . . to be back in school with my friends . . .

(*As the last lines are being said, the curtain rises on the scene. The lights dim on as* ANNE'S VOICE *fades away.*)

Scene V

It is the first night of the Hanukkah[13] celebration. MR. FRANK *is standing at the head of the table on which is the Menorah.[14] He lights the Shamos, or servant candle, and holds it as he says the blessing. Seated listening is all of the "family," dressed in their best. The men wear hats,* PETER *wears his cap.*

MR. FRANK

(Reading from a prayer book)

"Praised be Thou, oh Lord our God, Ruler of the universe, who has sanctified us with Thy commandments and bidden us kindle the Hanukkah lights. Praised be Thou, oh Lord our God, Ruler of the universe, who has wrought wondrous deliverances for our fathers in days of old. Praised be Thou, oh Lord our God, Ruler of the universe, that Thou has given us life and sustenance and brought us to this happy season." (MR. FRANK *lights the one candle of the Menorah as he continues*) "We kindle this Hanukkah light to celebrate the great and wonderful deeds wrought through the zeal with which God filled the hearts of the heroic Maccabees, two thousand years ago. They fought against indifference, against tyranny and oppression, and they restored our Temple to us. May these lights remind us that we should ever look to God, whence cometh our help." Amen. [Pronounced O-mayn.]

---

[13]*Hanukkah:* traditional Jewish festival.
[14]*Menorah:* special candle-holder for the Hanukkah candles.

ALL

Amen.

(MR. FRANK *hands* MRS. FRANK *the prayer book.*)

MRS. FRANK

(*Reading*)

"I lift up mine eyes unto the mountains, from whence cometh my help. My help cometh from the Lord who made heaven and earth. He will not suffer thy foot to be moved. He that keepeth thee will not slumber. He that keepeth Israel doth neither slumber nor sleep. The Lord is thy keeper. The Lord is thy shade upon thy right hand. The sun shall not smite thee by day, nor the moon by night. The Lord shall keep thee from all evil. He shall keep thy soul. The Lord shall guard thy going out and thy coming in, from this time forth and forevermore." Amen.

ALL

Amen.

(MRS. FRANK *puts down the prayer book and goes to get the food and wine.* MARGOT *helps her.* MR. FRANK *takes the men's hats and puts them aside.*)

DUSSEL

(*Rising*)

That was very moving.

ANNE

(*Pulling him back*)

It isn't over yet!

MRS. VAN DAAN

Sit down! Sit down!

ANNE

There's a lot more, songs and presents.

DUSSEL

Presents?

MRS. FRANK

Not this year, unfortunately.

MRS. VAN DAAN

But always on Hanukkah everyone gives presents . . . everyone!

DUSSEL

Like our St. Nicholas' Day.[15]
(*There is a chorus of "no's" from the group.*)

MRS. VAN DAAN

No! Not like St. Nicholas! What kind of a Jew are you that you don't know Hanukkah?

MRS. FRANK

(*As she brings the food*)
I remember particularly the candles . . . First one, as we have tonight. Then the second night you light two candles, the next night three . . . and so on until you have eight candles burning. When there are eight candles it is truly beautiful.

---

[15]*our St. Nicholas' Day:* Often a person would have adopted another culture and religion, as Mr. Dussel seems to have done, and would find out that he or she was "legally" Jewish only when Nazi persecutions began.

MRS. VAN DAAN

And the potato pancakes.

MR. VAN DAAN

Don't talk about them!

MRS. VAN DAAN

I make the best *latkes* you ever tasted!

MRS. FRANK

Invite us all next year . . . in your own home.

MR. FRANK

God willing!

MRS. VAN DAAN

God willing.

MARGOT

What I remember best is the presents we used to get when we were little . . . eight days of presents . . . and each day they got better and better.

MRS. FRANK

(*Sitting down*)
We are all here, alive. That is present enough.

ANNE

No, it isn't. I've got something . . .
(*She rushes into her room, hurriedly puts on a little hat improvised from the lamp shade, grabs a satchel bulging with parcels and comes running back.*)

MRS. FRANK

What is it?

ANNE

Presents!

MRS. VAN DAAN

Presents!

DUSSEL

Look!

MR. VAN DAAN

What's she got on her head?

PETER

A lamp shade!

ANNE

(*She picks out one at random*)

This is for Margot. (*She hands it to* MARGOT, *pulling her to her feet*) Read it out loud.

MARGOT

(*Reading*)

"You have never lost your temper.
  You never will, I fear,
  You are so good.
  But if you should,
  Put all your cross words here."

(*She tears open the package*)

A new crossword puzzle book! Where did you get it?

ANNE

It isn't new. It's one that you've done. But I rubbed it all out, and if you wait a little and forget, you can do it all over again.

MARGOT

(*Sitting*)

It's wonderful, Anne. Thank you. You'd never know it wasn't new.

(*From outside we hear the sound of a streetcar passing.*)

ANNE

(*With another gift*)

Mrs. Van Daan.

MRS. VAN DAAN

(*Taking it*)

This is awful . . . I haven't anything for anyone . . . I never thought . . .

MR. FRANK

This is all Anne's idea.

MRS. VAN DAAN

(*Holding up a bottle*)

What is it?

ANNE

It's hair shampoo. I took all the odds and ends of soap and mixed them with the last of my toilet water.

MRS. VAN DAAN

Oh, Anneke!

ANNE

I wanted to write a poem for all of them, but I didn't have time. (*Offering a large box to* MR. VAN DAAN) Yours, Mr. Van Daan, is *really* something . . . something you want more than anything. (*As she waits for him to open it*) Look! Cigarettes!

MR. VAN DAAN

Cigarettes!

ANNE

Two of them! Pim found some old pipe tobacco in the pocket lining of his coat . . . and we made them . . . or rather, Pim did.

MRS. VAN DAAN

Let me see . . . Well, look at that! Light it, Putti! Light it. (MR. VAN DAAN *hesitates*.)

ANNE

It's tobacco, really it is! There's a little fluff in it, but not much. (*Everyone watches intently as* MR. VAN DAAN *cautiously lights it. The cigarette flares up. Everyone laughs.*)

PETER

It works!

MRS. VAN DAAN

Look at him.

MR. VAN DAAN

(*Spluttering*)

Thank you, Anne. Thank you. (ANNE *rushes back to her satchel for another present.*)

ANNE

(*Handing her mother a piece of paper*)

For Mother, Hanukkah greeting.

(*She pulls her mother to her feet.*)

MRS. FRANK

(*She reads*)

"Here's an I.O.U. that I promise to pay.

Ten hours of doing whatever you say. Signed, Anne Frank."

(MRS. FRANK, *touched, takes* ANNE *in her arms, holding her close.*)

DUSSEL

(*To* ANNE)

Ten hours of doing what you're told? *Anything* you're told?

ANNE

That's right.

DUSSEL

You wouldn't want to sell that, Mrs. Frank?

MRS. FRANK

Never! This is the most precious gift I've ever had!

(*She sits, showing her present to the others.* ANNE *hurries back to the satchel and pulls out a scarf, the scarf that* MR. FRANK *found in the first scene.*)

ANNE

(*Offering it to her father*)

For Pim.

MR. FRANK

Anneke . . . I wasn't supposed to have a present!
(*He takes it, unfolding it and showing it to the others.*)

ANNE

It's a muffler . . . to put round your neck . . . like an ascot, you know. I made it myself out of odds and ends . . . I knitted it in the dark each night, after I'd gone to bed. I'm afraid it looks better in the dark!

MR. FRANK

(*Putting it on*)

It's fine. It fits me perfectly. Thank you, Anneke.
(ANNE *hands* PETER *a ball of paper, with a string attached to it.*)

ANNE

That's for Mouschi.

PETER

(*Rising to bow*)

On behalf of Mouschi, I thank you.

ANNE

(*Hesitant, handing him a gift*)

And . . . this is yours . . . from Mrs. Quack Quack. (*As he holds it gingerly in his hands*) Well . . . open it . . . Aren't you going to open it?

PETER

I'm scared to. I know something's going to jump out and hit me.

ANNE

No. It's nothing like that, really.

MRS. VAN DAAN

(*As he is opening it*)

What is it, Peter? Go on. Show it.

ANNE

(*Excitedly*)

It's a safety razor!

DUSSEL

A what?

ANNE

A razor!

MRS. VAN DAAN

(*Looking at it*)

You didn't make that out of odds and ends.

ANNE

(*To* PETER)

Miep got it for me. It's not new. It's second-hand. But you really do need a razor now.

DUSSEL

For what?

ANNE

Look on his upper lip . . . you can see the beginning of a mustache.

DUSSEL

He wants to get rid of that? Put a little milk on it and let the
cat lick it off.

PETER

(*Starting for his room*)

Think you're funny, don't you.

DUSSEL

Look! He can't wait! He's going in to try it!

PETER

I'm going to give Mouschi his present!
(*He goes into his room, slamming the door behind him.*)

MR. VAN DAAN

(*Disgustedly*)

Mouschi, Mouschi, Mouschi.
(*In the distance we hear a dog persistently barking.* ANNE
brings a gift to DUSSEL.)

ANNE

And last but never least, my roommate, Mr. Dussel.

DUSSEL

For me? You have something for me?
(*He opens the small box she gives him.*)

ANNE

I made them myself.

DUSSEL

(Puzzled)

Capsules! Two capsules!

ANNE

They're ear-plugs!

DUSSEL

Ear-plugs?

ANNE

To put in your ears so you won't hear me when I thrash around at night. I saw them advertised in a magazine. They're not real ones . . . I made them out of cotton and candle wax. Try them . . . See if they don't work . . . see if you can hear me talk . . .

DUSSEL

(Putting them in his ears)

Wait now until I get them in . . . so.

ANNE

Are you ready?

DUSSEL

Huh?

ANNE

Are you ready?

DUSSEL

Good God! They've gone inside! I can't get them out! (*They laugh as* MR. DUSSEL *jumps about, trying to shake the plugs out of his ears. Finally he gets them out. Putting them away)* Thank you, Anne! Thank you!

MR. VAN DAAN

A real Hanukkah!

MRS. VAN DAAN

Wasn't it cute of her?

Together

MRS. FRANK

I don't know when she did it.

MARGOT

I love my present.

ANNE

(Sitting at the table)

And now let's have the song, Father . . . please . . . *(To* DUSSEL*)* Have you heard the Hanukkah song, Mr. Dussel? The song is the whole thing! *(She sings)* "Oh, Hanukkah! Oh Hanukkah! The sweet celebration . . ."

MR. FRANK

(Quieting her)

I'm afraid, Anne, we shouldn't sing that song tonight. *(To* DUSSEL*)* It's a song of jubilation, of rejoicing. One is apt to become too enthusiastic.

ANNE

Oh, please, please. Let's sing the song. I promise not to shout!

MR. FRANK

Very well. But quietly now . . . I'll keep an eye on you and when . . .

(As ANNE *starts to sing, she is interrupted by* DUSSEL, *who is snorting and wheezing.)*

DUSSEL

(Pointing to PETER*)*

You . . . You! (PETER *is coming from his bedroom, ostentatiously holding a bulge in his coat as if he were holding his cat, and dangling* ANNE's *present before it)* How many times . . . I told you . . . Out! Out!

MR. VAN DAAN

(Going to PETER*)*

What's the matter with you? Haven't you any sense? Get that cat out of here.

PETER

(Innocently)

Cat?

MR. VAN DAAN

You heard me. Get it out of here!

PETER

I have no cat.

(Delighted with his joke, he opens his coat and pulls out a bath towel. The group at the table laugh, enjoying the joke.)

DUSSEL

(*Still wheezing*)

It doesn't need to be the cat . . . his clothes are enough . . . when he comes out of that room . . .

MR. VAN DAAN

Don't worry. You won't be bothered any more. We're getting rid of it.

DUSSEL

At last you listen to me.

(*He goes off into his bedroom.*)

MR. VAN DAAN

(*Calling after him*)

I'm not doing it for you. That's all in your mind . . . all of it! (*He starts back to his place at the table*) I'm doing it because I'm sick of seeing that cat eat all our food.

PETER

That's not true! I only give him bones . . . scraps . . .

MR. VAN DAAN

Don't tell me! He gets fatter every day! Damn cat looks better than any of us. Out he goes tonight!

PETER

No! No!

ANNE

Mr. Van Daan, you can't do that! That's Peter's cat. Peter loves that cat.

MRS. FRANK
(*Quietly*)

Anne.

PETER
(*To* MR. VAN DAAN)

If he goes, I go.

MR. VAN DAAN

Go! Go!

MRS. VAN DAAN

You're not going and the cat's not going! Now please . . . this is Hanukkah . . . Hanukkah . . . this is the time to celebrate . . . What's the matter with all of you? Come on, Anne. Let's have the song.

ANNE
(*Singing*)

"Oh, Hanukkah! Oh, Hanukkah!
The sweet celebration."

MR. FRANK
(*Rising*)

I think we should first blow out the candle . . . then we'll have something for tomorrow night.

MARGOT

But, Father, you're supposed to let it burn itself out.

MR. FRANK

I'm sure that God understands shortages. (*Before blowing it out*) "Praised be Thou, oh Lord our God, who hast sustained us and permitted us to celebrate this joyous festival."

(*He is about to blow out the candle when suddenly there is a crash of something falling below. They all freeze in horror, motionless. For a few seconds there is complete silence.* MR. FRANK *slips off his shoes. The others noiselessly follow his example.* MR. FRANK *turns out a light near him. He motions to* PETER *to turn off the center lamp.* PETER *tries to reach it, realizes he cannot and gets up on a chair. Just as he is touching the lamp he loses his balance. The chair goes out from under him. He falls. The iron lamp shade crashes to the floor. There is a sound of feet below, running down the stairs.*)

MR. VAN DAAN

(*Under his breath*)

God Almighty! (*The only light left comes from the Hanukkah candle.* DUSSEL *comes from his room.* MR. FRANK *creeps over to the stairwell and stands listening. The dog is heard barking excitedly*) Do you hear anything?

MR. FRANK

(*In a whisper*)

No. I think they've gone.

MRS. VAN DAAN

It's the Green Police. They've found us.

MR. FRANK

If they had, they wouldn't have left. They'd be up here by now.

MRS. VAN DAAN

I know it's the Green Police. They've gone to get help. That's all. They'll be back!

MR. VAN DAAN

Or it may have been the Gestapo,[16] looking for papers . . .

MR. FRANK

(*Interrupting*)

Or a thief, looking for money.

MRS. VAN DAAN

We've got to do something . . . Quick! Quick! Before they come back.

MR. VAN DAAN

There isn't anything to do. Just wait.

(MR. FRANK *holds up his hand for them to be quiet. He is listening intently. There is complete silence as they all strain to hear any sound from below. Suddenly* ANNE *begins to sway. With a low cry she falls to the floor in a faint.* MRS. FRANK *goes to her quickly, sitting beside her on the floor and taking her in her arms.*)

---

[16]*Gestapo:* Nazi secret police.

MRS. FRANK

Get some water, please! Get some water!
(MARGOT *starts for the sink.*)

MR. VAN DAAN

(*Grabbing* MARGOT)
No! No! No one's going to run water!

MR. FRANK

If they've found us, they've found us. Get the water. (MARGOT *starts again for the sink.* MR. FRANK, *getting a flashlight*) I'm going down.

(MARGOT *rushes to him, clinging to him.* ANNE *struggles to consciousness.*)

MARGOT

No, Father, no! There may be someone there, waiting . . . It may be a trap!

MR. FRANK

This is Saturday. There is no way for us to know what has happened until Miep or Mr. Kraler comes on Monday morning. We cannot live with this uncertainty.

MARGOT

Don't go, Father!

MRS. FRANK

Hush, darling, hush. (MR. FRANK *slips quietly out, down the steps and out through the door below*) Margot! Stay close to me.
(MARGOT *goes to her mother.*)

MR. VAN DAAN

Shush! Shush!

(MRS. FRANK *whispers to* MARGOT *to get the water.* MARGOT *goes for it.*)

MRS. VAN DAAN

Putti, where's our money? Get our money. I hear you can buy the Green Police off, so much a head. Go upstairs quick! Get the money!

MR. VAN DAAN

Keep still!

MRS. VAN DAAN

(*Kneeling before him, pleading*)

Do you want to be dragged off to a concentration camp? Are you going to stand there and wait for them to come up and get you? Do something, I tell you!

MR. VAN DAAN

(*Pushing her aside*)

Will you keep still!

(*He goes over to the stairwell to listen.* PETER *goes to his mother, helping her up onto the sofa. There is a second of silence, then* ANNE *can stand it no longer.*)

ANNE

Someone go after Father! Make Father come back!

PETER

(*Starting for the door*)

I'll go.

MR. VAN DAAN

Haven't you done enough?

(*He pushes* PETER *roughly away. In his anger against his father* PETER *grabs a chair as if to hit him with it, then puts it down, burying his face in his hands.* MRS. FRANK *begins to pray softly.*)

ANNE

Please, please, Mr. Van Daan. Get Father.

MR. VAN DAAN

Quiet! Quiet!

(ANNE *is shocked into silence.* MRS. FRANK *pulls her closer, holding her protectively in her arms.*)

MRS. FRANK

(*Softly, praying*)

"I lift up mine eyes unto the mountains, from whence cometh my help. My help cometh from the Lord who made heaven and earth. He will not suffer thy foot to be moved . . . He that keepeth thee will not slumber . . ."

(*She stops as she hears someone coming. They all watch the door tensely.* MR. FRANK *comes quietly in.* ANNE *rushes to him, holding him tight.*)

MR. FRANK

It was a thief. That noise must have scared him away.

MRS. VAN DAAN

Thank God.

MR. FRANK

He took the cash box. And the radio. He ran away in such a hurry that he didn't stop to shut the street door. It was swinging wide open. (*A breath of relief sweeps over them*) I think it would be good to have some light.

MARGOT

Are you sure it's all right?

MR. FRANK

The danger has passed. (MARGOT *goes to light the small lamp*) Don't be so terrified, Anne. We're safe.

DUSSEL

Who says the danger has passed? Don't you realize we are in greater danger than ever?

MR. FRANK

Mr. Dussel, will you be still!

(MR. FRANK *takes* ANNE *back to the table, making her sit down with him, trying to calm her.*)

DUSSEL

(*Pointing to* PETER)

Thanks to this clumsy fool, there's someone now who knows we're up here! Someone now knows we're up here, hiding!

MRS. VAN DAAN

(*Going to* DUSSEL)

Someone knows we're here, yes. But who is the someone? A thief! A thief! You think a thief is going to go to the Green

Police and say . . . I was robbing a place the other night and I heard a noise up over my head? You think a thief is going to do that?

DUSSEL

Yes. I think he will.

MRS. VAN DAAN

(*Hysterically*)

You're crazy!

(*She stumbles back to her seat at the table.* PETER *follows protectively, pushing* DUSSEL *aside.*)

DUSSEL

I think some day he'll be caught and then he'll make a bargain with the Green Police . . . if they'll let him off, he'll tell them where some Jews are hiding!

(*He goes off into the bedroom. There is a second of appalled silence.*)

MR. VAN DAAN

He's right.

ANNE

Father, let's get out of here! We can't stay here now . . . Let's go . . .

MR. VAN DAAN

Go! Where?

MRS. FRANK

(*Sinking into her chair at the table*)

Yes. Where?

MR. FRANK

(*Rising, to them all*)

Have we lost all faith? All courage? A moment ago we thought that they'd come for us. We were sure it was the end. But it wasn't the end. We're alive, safe. (MR. VAN DAAN *goes to the table and sits.* MR. FRANK *prays*) "We thank Thee, oh Lord our God, that in Thy infinite mercy Thou hast again seen fit to spare us." (*He blows out the candle, then turns to* ANNE) Come on, Anne. The song! Let's have the song! (*He starts to sing.* ANNE *finally starts falteringly to sing, as* MR. FRANK *urges her on. Her voice is hardly audible at first.*)

ANNE

(*Singing*)

"Oh, Hanukkah! Oh, Hanukkah!
The sweet . . . celebration . . ."

(*As she goes on singing, the others gradually join in, their voices still shaking with fear.* MRS. VAN DAAN *sobs as she sings.*)

GROUP

"Around the feast . . . we . . . gather
In complete . . . jubilation . . .
Happiest of sea . . . sons
Now is here.
Many are the reasons for good cheer."

(DUSSEL *comes from the bedroom. He comes over to the table, standing beside* MARGOT, *listening to them as they sing.*)

"Together

We'll weather

Whatever tomorrow may bring."

    (*As they sing on with growing courage, the lights start to dim*)

"So hear us rejoicing

And merrily voicing

The Hanukkah song that we sing.

Hoy!"

    (*The lights are out. The curtain starts slowly to fall*)

"Hear us rejoicing

And merrily voicing

The Hanukkah song that we sing."

    (*They are still singing, as the curtain falls.*)

Curtain

ACT TWO

ACT TWO

Scene I

In the darkness we hear ANNE'S VOICE, *again reading from the diary.*

ANNE'S VOICE

Saturday, the first of January, nineteen forty-four. Another new year has begun and we find ourselves still in our hiding place. We have been here now for one year, five months and twenty-five days. It seems that our life is at a standstill.

The curtain rises on the scene. It is late afternoon. Everyone is bundled up against the cold. In the main room MRS. FRANK *is taking down the laundry which is hung across the back.* MR. FRANK *sits in the chair down left, reading.* MARGOT *is lying on the couch with a blanket over her and the many-colored knitted scarf around her throat.* ANNE *is seated at the center table, writing in her diary.* PETER, MR. *and* MRS. VAN DAAN *and* DUSSEL *are all in their own rooms, reading or lying down.*

As the lights dim on, ANNE'S VOICE *continues, without a break.*

ANNE'S VOICE

We are all a little thinner. The Van Daans' "discussions" are as violent as ever. Mother still does not understand me. But then I don't understand her either. There is one great change, however. A change in myself. I read somewhere that girls of my age don't feel quite certain of themselves. That they become quiet within and begin to think of the miracle that is taking place in their bodies. I think that what is happening to me is so wonderful . . . not only what can be seen, but what is taking place inside. Each time it has happened I have a feeling that I have a sweet secret. (*We hear the chimes and then a hymn being played on the carillon outside*) And in spite of any pain, I long for the time when I shall feel that secret within me again.

(*The buzzer of the door below suddenly sounds. Everyone is startled,* MR. FRANK *tiptoes cautiously to the top of the steps and listens. Again the buzzer sounds, in* MIEP's *V-for-Victory signal.*)

MR. FRANK

It's Miep!

(*He goes quickly down the steps to unbolt the door.* MRS. FRANK *calls upstairs to the* VAN DAANS *and then to* PETER.)

MRS. FRANK

Wake up, everyone! Miep is here! (ANNE *quickly puts her diary away.* MARGOT *sits up, pulling the blanket around her shoulders.* MR. DUSSEL *sits on the edge of his bed, listening, disgruntled.* MIEP *comes up the steps, followed by* MR. KRALER. *They bring flowers, books, newspapers, etc.* ANNE *rushes to* MIEP, *throwing her arms affectionately around her*) Miep . . . and Mr. Kraler . . . What a delightful surprise!

MR. KRALER

We came to bring you New Year's greetings.

MRS. FRANK

You shouldn't . . . you should have at least one day to your-selves.

(*She goes quickly to the stove and brings down teacups and tea for all of them.*)

ANNE

Don't say that, it's so wonderful to see them! (*Sniffing at* MIEP's *coat*) I can smell the wind and the cold on your clothes.

MIEP

(*Giving her the flowers*)

There you are. (*Then to* MARGOT, *feeling her forehead*) How are you, Margot? . . . Feeling any better?

MARGOT

I'm all right.

ANNE

We filled her full of every kind of pill so she won't cough and make a noise.

(*She runs into her room to put the flowers in water.* MR. *and* MRS. VAN DAAN *come from upstairs. Outside there is the sound of a band playing.*)

MRS. VAN DAAN

Well, hello, Miep. Mr. Kraler.

MR. KRALER

(*Giving a bouquet of flowers to* MRS. VAN DAAN)

With my hope for peace in the New Year.

PETER

(*Anxiously*)

Miep, have you seen Mouschi? Have you seen him anywhere around?

MIEP

I'm sorry, Peter. I asked everyone in the neighborhood had they seen a gray cat. But they said no.

(MRS. FRANK *gives* MIEP *a cup of tea.* MR. FRANK *comes up the steps, carrying a small cake on a plate.*)

MR. FRANK

Look what Miep's brought for us!

MRS. FRANK

(*Taking it*)

A cake!

MR. VAN DAAN

A cake! (*He pinches* MIEP's *cheeks gaily and hurries up to the cupboard*) I'll get some plates.

(DUSSEL, *in his room, hastily puts a coat on and starts out to join the others.*)

MRS. FRANK

Thank you, Miepia. You shouldn't have done it. You must have used all of your sugar ration for weeks. (*Giving it to* MRS. VAN DAAN) It's beautiful, isn't it?

MRS. VAN DAAN

It's been ages since I even saw a cake. Not since you brought us one last year. (*Without looking at the cake, to* MIEP) Remember? Don't you remember, you gave us one on New Year's Day? Just this time last year? I'll never forget it because you had "Peace in nineteen forty-three" on it. (*She looks at the cake and reads*) "Peace in nineteen forty-four!"

MIEP

Well, it has to come sometime, you know. (*As* DUSSEL *comes from his room*) Hello, Mr. Dussel.

MR. KRALER

How are you?

MR. VAN DAAN

(*Bringing plates and a knife*)
Here's the knife, *liefje*. Now, how many of us are there?

MIEP

None for me, thank you.

MR. FRANK

Oh, please. You must.

MIEP

I couldn't.

MR. VAN DAAN

Good! That leaves one . . . two . . . three . . . seven of us.

DUSSEL

Eight! Eight! It's the same number as it always is!

MR. VAN DAAN

I left Margot out. I take it for granted Margot won't eat any.

ANNE

Why wouldn't she!

MRS. FRANK

I think it won't harm her.

MR. VAN DAAN

All right! All right! I just didn't want her to start coughing again, that's all.

DUSSEL

And please, Mrs. Frank should cut the cake.

MR. VAN DAAN

What's the difference?

MRS. VAN DAAN

It's not Mrs. Frank's cake, is it, Miep? It's for all of us.

Together

DUSSEL

Mrs. Frank divides things better.

MRS. VAN DAAN
(*Going to* DUSSEL)

What are you trying to say?

Together

MR. VAN DAAN

Oh, come on! Stop wasting time!

MRS. VAN DAAN

(*To* DUSSEL)

Don't I always give everybody exactly the same? Don't I?

MR. VAN DAAN

Forget it, Kerli.

MRS. VAN DAAN

No. I want an answer! Don't I?

DUSSEL

Yes. Yes. Everybody gets exactly the same . . . except Mr. Van Daan always gets a little bit more.

(VAN DAAN *advances on* DUSSEL, *the knife still in his hand.*)

MR. VAN DAAN

That's a lie!

(DUSSEL *retreats before the onslaught of the* VAN DAANS.)

MR. FRANK

Please, please! (*Then to* MIEP) You see what a little sugar cake does to us? It goes right to our heads!

MR. VAN DAAN

(*Handing* MRS. FRANK *the knife*)

Here you are, Mrs. Frank.

MRS. FRANK

Thank you. (*Then to* MIEP *as she goes to the table to cut the cake*) Are you sure you won't have some?

MIEP

(Drinking her tea)

No, really, I have to go in a minute.

(The sound of the band fades out in the distance.)

PETER

(To MIEP*)*

Maybe Mouschi went back to our house . . . they say that cats . . . Do you ever get over there . . . ? I mean . . . do you suppose you could . . . ?

MIEP

I'll try, Peter. The first minute I get I'll try. But I'm afraid, with him gone a week . . .

DUSSEL

Make up your mind, already someone has had a nice big dinner from that cat!

*(*PETER *is furious, inarticulate. He starts toward* DUSSEL *as if to hit him.* MR. FRANK *stops him.* MRS. FRANK *speaks quickly to ease the situation.)*

MRS. FRANK

(To MIEP*)*

This is delicious, Miep!

MRS. VAN DAAN

(Eating hers)

Delicious!

MR. VAN DAAN

(Finishing it in one gulp)

Dirk's in luck to get a girl who can bake like this!

MIEP

(*Putting down her empty teacup*)
I have to run. Dirk's taking me to a party tonight.

ANNE

How heavenly! Remember now what everyone is wearing, and what you have to eat and everything, so you can tell us to-morrow.

MIEP

I'll give you a full report! Good-bye, everyone!

MR. VAN DAAN

(*To* MIEP)
Just a minute. There's something I'd like you to do for me.
(*He hurries off up the stairs to his room.*)

MRS. VAN DAAN

(*Sharply*)
Putti, where are you going? (*She rushes up the stairs after him, calling hysterically*) What do you want? Putti, what are you going to do?

MIEP

(*To* PETER)
What's wrong?

PETER

(*His sympathy is with his mother*)
Father says he's going to sell her fur coat. She's crazy about that old fur coat.

DUSSEL

Is it possible? Is it possible that anyone is so silly as to worry about a fur coat in times like this?

PETER

It's none of your darn business . . . and if you say one more thing . . . I'll, I'll take you and I'll . . . I mean it . . . I'll . . .
(*There is a piercing scream from* MRS. VAN DAAN *above. She grabs at the fur coat as* MR. VAN DAAN *is starting downstairs with it.*)

MRS. VAN DAAN

No! No! No! Don't you dare take that! You hear? It's mine! (*Downstairs* PETER *turns away, embarrassed, miserable*) My father gave me that! You didn't give it to me. You have no right. Let go of it . . . you hear?
(MR. VAN DAAN *pulls the coat from her hands and hurries downstairs.* MRS. VAN DAAN *sinks to the floor, sobbing. As* MR. VAN DAAN *comes into the main room the others look away, embarrassed for him.*)

MR. VAN DAAN
(*To* MR. KRALER)

Just a little—discussion over the advisability of selling this coat. As I have often reminded Mrs. Van Daan, it's very selfish of her to keep it when people outside are in such desperate need of clothing . . . (*He gives the coat to* MIEP) So if you will please to sell it for us? It should fetch a good price. And by the way, will you get me cigarettes. I don't care what kind they are . . . get all you can.

MIEP

It's terribly difficult to get them, Mr. Van Daan. But I'll try. Good-bye.

(*She goes.* MR. FRANK *follows her down the steps to bolt the door after her.* MRS. FRANK *gives* MR. KRALER *a cup of tea.*)

MRS. FRANK

Are you sure you won't have some cake, Mr. Kraler?

MR. KRALER

I'd better not.

MR. VAN DAAN

You're still feeling badly? What does your doctor say?

MR. KRALER

I haven't been to him.

MRS. FRANK

Now, Mr. Kraler! . . .

MR. KRALER

(*Sitting at the table*)

Oh, I tried. But you can't get near a doctor these days . . . they're so busy. After weeks I finally managed to get one on the telephone. I told him I'd like an appointment . . . I wasn't feeling very well. You know what he answers . . . over the telephone . . . Stick out your tongue! (*They laugh. He turns to* MR. FRANK *as* MR. FRANK *comes back*) I have some contracts here . . . I wonder if you'd look over them with me . . .

MR. FRANK

(*Putting out his hand*)

Of course.

MR. KRALER

(*He rises*)

If we could go downstairs . . . (MR. FRANK *starts ahead,* MR. KRALER *speaks to the others*) Will you forgive us? I won't keep him but a minute.

(*He starts to follow* MR. FRANK *down the steps.*)

MARGOT

(*With sudden foreboding*)

What's happened? Something's happened! Hasn't it, Mr. Kraler?

(MR. KRALER *stops and comes back, trying to reassure* MARGOT *with a pretense of casualness.*)

MR. KRALER

No, really. I want your father's advice . . .

MARGOT

Something's gone wrong! I know it!

MR. FRANK

(*Coming back, to* MR. KRALER)

If it's something that concerns us here, it's better that we all hear it.

MR. KRALER

(Turning to him, quietly)

But . . . the children . . . ?

MR. FRANK

What they'd imagine would be worse than any reality.

(As MR. KRALER *speaks, they all listen with intense apprehension.* MRS. VAN DAAN *comes down the stairs and sits on the bottom step.)*

MR. KRALER

It's a man in the storeroom . . . I don't know whether or not you remember him . . . Carl, about fifty, heavy-set, near-sighted . . . He came with us just before you left.

MR. FRANK

He was from Utrecht?

MR. KRALER

That's the man. A couple of weeks ago, when I was in the storeroom, he closed the door and asked me . . . how's Mr. Frank? What do you hear from Mr. Frank? I told him I only knew there was a rumor that you were in Switzerland. He said he'd heard that rumor too, but he thought I might know something more. I didn't pay any attention to it . . . but then a thing happened yesterday . . . He'd brought some invoices to the office for me to sign. As I was going through them, I looked up. He was standing staring at the bookcase . . . your bookcase. He said he thought he remembered a door there . . . Wasn't there a door there that used to go up to the loft? Then he told me he wanted more money. Twenty guilders more a week.

MR. VAN DAAN

Blackmail!

MR. FRANK

Twenty guilders? Very modest blackmail.

MR. VAN DAAN

That's just the beginning.

DUSSEL

(*Coming to* MR. FRANK)

You know what I think? He was the thief who was down there that night. That's how he knows we're here.

MR. FRANK

(*To* MR. KRALER)

How was it left? What did you tell him?

MR. KRALER

I said I had to think about it. What shall I do? Pay him the money? . . . Take a chance on firing him . . . or what? I don't know.

DUSSEL

(*Frantic*)

For God's sake don't fire him! Pay him what he asks . . . keep him here where you can have your eye on him.

MR. FRANK

Is it so much that he's asking? What are they paying nowadays?

MR. KRALER

He could get it in a war plant. But this isn't a war plant. Mind you, I don't know if he really knows . . . or if he doesn't know.

MR. FRANK

Offer him half. Then we'll soon find out if it's blackmail or not.

DUSSEL

And if it is? We've got to pay it, haven't we? Anything he asks we've got to pay!

MR. FRANK

Let's decide that when the time comes.

MR. KRALER

This may be all my imagination. You get to a point, these days, where you suspect everyone and everything. Again and again . . . on some simple look or word, I've found myself . . .

(*The telephone rings in the office below.*)

MRS. VAN DAAN

(*Hurrying to* MR. KRALER)

There's the telephone! What does that mean, the telephone ringing on a holiday?

MR. KRALER

That's my wife. I told her I had to go over some papers in my office . . . to call me there when she got out of church. (*He starts out*) I'll offer him half then. Good-bye . . . we'll hope for the best!

(*The group call their good-bye's half-heartedly.* MR. FRANK *follows* MR. KRALER, *to bolt the door below. During the following scene,* MR. FRANK *comes back up and stands listening, disturbed.*)

DUSSEL

(*To* MR. VAN DAAN)

You can thank your son for this . . . smashing the light! I tell you, it's just a question of time now.

(*He goes to the window at the back and stands looking out.*)

MARGOT

Sometimes I wish the end would come . . . whatever it is.

MRS. FRANK

(*Shocked*)

Margot!

(ANNE *goes to* MARGOT, *sitting beside her on the couch with her arms around her.*)

MARGOT

Then at least we'd know where we were.

MRS. FRANK

You should be ashamed of yourself! Talking that way! Think how lucky we are! Think of the thousands dying in the war, every day. Think of the people in concentration camps.

ANNE

(*Interrupting*)

What's the good of that? What's the good of thinking of misery when you're already miserable? That's stupid!

MRS. FRANK

Anne!

(*As* ANNE *goes on raging at her mother,* MRS. FRANK *tries to break in, in an effort to quiet her.*)

ANNE

We're young, Margot and Peter and I! You grownups have had your chance! But look at us . . . If we begin thinking of all the horror in the world, we're lost! We're trying to hold onto some kind of ideals . . . when everything . . . ideals, hopes . . . everything, are being destroyed! It isn't our fault that the world is in such a mess! We weren't around when all this started! So don't try to take it out on us!

(*She rushes off to her room, slamming the door after her. She picks up a brush from the chest and hurls it to the floor. Then she sits on the settee, trying to control her anger.*)

MR. VAN DAAN

She talks as if we started the war! Did we start the war?

(*He spots* ANNE'S *cake. As he starts to take it,* PETER *antici- pates him.*)

PETER

She left her cake. (*He starts for* ANNE'S *room with the cake. There is silence in the main room.* MRS. VAN DAAN *goes up to her room, followed by* VAN DAAN. DUSSEL *stays looking out the window.* MR. FRANK *brings* MRS. FRANK *her cake. She eats it slowly, without relish.* MR. FRANK *takes his cake to* MARGOT *and sits quietly on the sofa beside her.* PETER *stands in the doorway of* ANNE'S *darkened room, looking at her, then makes a little movement to let her know he is there.* ANNE *sits up, quickly, trying to hide the signs of her tears.* PETER *holds out the cake to her.*) You left this.

ANNE
(*Dully*)
Thanks.
(PETER *starts to go out, then comes back.*)

PETER

I thought you were fine just now. You know just how to talk to them. You know just how to say it. I'm no good . . . I never can think . . . especially when I'm mad . . . That Dussel . . . when he said that about Mouschi . . . someone eating him . . . all I could think is . . . I wanted to hit him. I wanted to give him such a . . . a . . . that he'd . . . That's what I used to do when there was an argument at school . . . That's the way I . . . but here . . . And an old man like that . . . it wouldn't be so good.

ANNE

You're making a big mistake about me. I do it all wrong. I say too much. I go too far. I hurt people's feelings . . .
(DUSSEL *leaves the window, going to his room.*)

PETER

I think you're just fine . . . What I want to say . . . if it wasn't for you around here, I don't know. What I mean . . .
(PETER *is interrupted by* DUSSEL'S *turning on the light.* DUSSEL *stands in the doorway, startled to see* PETER. PETER

advances toward him forbiddingly. DUSSEL *backs out of the room.* PETER *closes the door on him.*)

ANNE

Do you mean it, Peter? Do you really mean it?

PETER

I said it, didn't I?

ANNE

Thank you, Peter!
(*In the main room* MR. *and* MRS. FRANK *collect the dishes and take them to the sink, washing them.* MARGOT *lies down again on the couch.* DUSSEL, *lost, wanders into* PETER's *room and takes up a book, starting to read.*)

PETER

(*Looking at the photographs on the wall*)
You've got quite a collection.

ANNE

Wouldn't you like some in your room? I could give you some. Heaven knows you spend enough time in there . . . doing heaven knows what . . .

PETER

It's easier. A fight starts, or an argument . . . I duck in there.

ANNE

You're lucky, having a room to go to. His lordship is always here . . . I hardly ever get a minute alone. When they start in on me, I can't duck away. I have to stand there and take it.

PETER

You gave some of it back just now.

ANNE

I get so mad. They've formed their opinions . . . about everything . . . but we . . . we're still trying to find out . . . We have problems here that no other people our age have ever had. And just as you think you've solved them, something comes along and bang! You have to start all over again.

PETER

At least you've got someone you can talk to.

ANNE

Not really. Mother . . . I never discuss anything serious with her. She doesn't understand. Father's all right. We can talk about everything . . . everything but one thing. Mother. He simply won't talk about her. I don't think you can be really intimate with anyone if he holds something back, do you?

PETER

I think your father's fine.

ANNE

Oh, he is, Peter! He is! He's the only one who's ever given me the feeling that I have any sense. But anyway, nothing can take the place of school and play and friends of your own age . . . or near your age . . . can it?

PETER

I suppose you miss your friends and all.

ANNE

It isn't just ... (*She breaks off, staring up at him for a second*) Isn't it funny, you and I? Here we've been seeing each other every minute for almost a year and a half, and this is the first time we've ever really talked. It helps a lot to have someone to talk to, don't you think? It helps you to let off steam.

PETER

(*Going to the door*)

Well, any time you want to let off steam, you can come into my room.

ANNE

(*Following him*)

I can get up an awful lot of steam. You'll have to be careful how you say that.

PETER

It's all right with me.

ANNE

Do you mean it?

PETER

I said it, didn't I?

(*He goes out.* ANNE *stands in her doorway looking after him. As* PETER *gets to his door he stands for a minute looking back at her. Then he goes into his room.* DUSSEL *rises as he comes in, and quickly passes him, going out. He starts across for his room.* ANNE *sees him coming, and pulls her door shut.* DUSSEL *turns back toward* PETER's *room.*

PETER *pulls his door shut.* DUSSEL *stands there, bewildered, forlorn.*

The scene slowly dims out. The curtain falls on the scene. ANNE'S VOICE *comes over in the darkness . . . faintly at first, and then with growing strength.*)

ANNE'S VOICE

We've had bad news. The people from whom Miep got our ration books have been arrested. So we have had to cut down on our food. Our stomachs are so empty that they rumble and make strange noises, all in different keys. Mr. Van Daan's is deep and low, like a bass fiddle. Mine is high, whistling like a flute. As we all sit around waiting for supper, it's like an orchestra tuning up. It only needs Toscanini to raise his baton and we'd be off in the Ride of the Valkyries. Monday, the sixth of March, nineteen forty-four. Mr. Kraler is in the hospital. It seems he has ulcers. Pim says we are his ulcers. Miep has to run the business and us too. The Americans have landed on the southern tip of Italy. Father looks for a quick finish to the war. Mr. Dussel is waiting every day for the warehouse man to demand more money. Have I been skipping too much from one subject to another? I can't help it. I feel that spring is coming. I feel it in my whole body and soul. I feel utterly confused. I am longing . . . so longing . . . for everything . . . for friends . . . for someone to talk to . . . someone who understands . . . someone young, who feels as I do . . .

(*As these last lines are being said, the curtain rises on the scene. The lights dim on.* ANNE'S VOICE *fades out.*)

Scene II

It is evening, after supper. From outside we hear the sound of children playing. The "grownups," with the exception of MR. VAN DAAN, *are all in the main room.* MRS. FRANK *is doing some mending,* MRS. VAN DAAN *is reading a fashion magazine.* MR. FRANK *is going over business accounts.* DUSSEL, *in his dentist's jacket, is pacing up and down, impatient to get into his bedroom.* MR. VAN DAAN *is upstairs working on a piece of embroidery in an embroidery frame.*

In his room PETER *is sitting before the mirror, smoothing his hair. As the scene goes on, he puts on his tie, brushes his coat and puts it on, preparing himself meticulously for a visit from* ANNE. *On his wall are now hung some of* ANNE'S *motion picture stars.*

In her room ANNE *too is getting dressed. She stands before the mirror in her slip, trying various ways of dressing her hair.* MARGOT *is seated on the sofa, hemming a skirt for* ANNE *to wear.*

In the main room DUSSEL *can stand it no longer. He comes over, rapping sharply on the door of his and* ANNE'S *bedroom.*

ANNE
(Calling to him)

No, no, Mr. Dussel! I am not dressed yet. (DUSSEL *walks away, furious, sitting down and burying his head in his hands.* ANNE *turns to* MARGOT) How is that? How does that look?

MARGOT
(Glancing at her briefly)

Fine.

ANNE

You didn't even look.

MARGOT

Of course I did. It's fine.

ANNE

Margot, tell me, am I terribly ugly?

MARGOT

Oh, stop fishing.

ANNE

No. No. Tell me.

MARGOT

Of course you're not. You've got nice eyes . . . and a lot of animation, and . . .

ANNE

A little vague, aren't you?

(*She reaches over and takes a brassière out of* MARGOT'S *sewing basket. She holds it up to herself, studying the effect in the mirror. Outside,* MRS. FRANK, *feeling sorry for* DUSSEL, *comes over, knocking at the girls' door.*)

MRS. FRANK

(*Outside*)

May I come in?

MARGOT

Come in, Mother.

MRS. FRANK

(*Shutting the door behind her*)

Mr. Dussel's impatient to get in here.

ANNE

(*Still with the brassière*)

Heavens, he takes the room for himself the entire day.

MRS. FRANK

(*Gently*)

Anne, dear, you're not going in again tonight to see Peter?

ANNE

(*Dignified*)

That is my intention.

MRS. FRANK

But you've already spent a great deal of time in there today.

ANNE

I was in there exactly twice. Once to get the dictionary, and then three-quarters of an hour before supper.

MRS. FRANK

Aren't you afraid you're disturbing him?

ANNE

Mother, I have some intuition.

MRS. FRANK

Then may I ask you this much, Anne. Please don't shut the door when you go in.

ANNE

You sound like Mrs. Van Daan!

(*She throws the brassière back in* MARGOT's *sewing basket and picks up her blouse, putting it on.*)

MRS. FRANK

No. No. I don't mean to suggest anything wrong. I only wish that you wouldn't expose yourself to criticism . . . that you wouldn't give Mrs. Van Daan the opportunity to be unpleasant.

ANNE

Mrs. Van Daan doesn't need an opportunity to be unpleasant!

MRS. FRANK

Everyone's on edge, worried about Mr. Kraler. This is one more thing . . .

ANNE

I'm sorry, Mother. I'm going to Peter's room. I'm not going to let Petronella Van Daan spoil our friendship.

(MRS. FRANK *hesitates for a second, then goes out, closing the door after her. She gets a pack of playing cards and sits at the center table, playing solitaire. In* ANNE's *room* MARGOT *hands the finished skirt to* ANNE. *As* ANNE *is putting it on,* MARGOT *takes off her high-heeled shoes and stuffs paper in the toes so that* ANNE *can wear them.*)

MARGOT

(*To* ANNE)

Why don't you two talk in the main room? It'd save a lot of trouble. It's hard on Mother, having to listen to those remarks from Mrs. Van Daan and not say a word.

ANNE

Why doesn't she say a word? I think it's ridiculous to take it and take it.

MARGOT

You don't understand Mother at all, do you? She can't talk back. She's not like you. It's just not in her nature to fight back.

ANNE

Anyway . . . the only one I worry about is you. I feel awfully guilty about you.

(*She sits on the stool near* MARGOT, *putting on* MARGOT's *high-heeled shoes.*)

MARGOT

What about?

ANNE

I mean, every time I go into Peter's room, I have a feeling I may be hurting you. (MARGOT *shakes her head*) I know if it were me, I'd be wild. I'd be desperately jealous, if it were me.

MARGOT

Well, I'm not.

ANNE

You don't feel badly? Really? Truly? You're not jealous?

MARGOT

Of course I'm jealous . . . jealous that you've got something to get up in the morning for . . . But jealous of you and Peter? No.

(ANNE *goes back to the mirror.*)

ANNE

Maybe there's nothing to be jealous of. Maybe he doesn't really like me. Maybe I'm just taking the place of his cat . . . (*She picks up a pair of short white gloves, putting them on*) Wouldn't you like to come in with us?

MARGOT

I have a book.

(*The sound of the children playing outside fades out. In the main room* DUSSEL *can stand it no longer. He jumps up, going to the bedroom door and knocking sharply.*)

DUSSEL

Will you please let me in my room!

ANNE

Just a minute, dear, dear Mr. Dussel. (*She picks up her Mother's pink stole and adjusts it elegantly over her shoulders, then gives a last look in the mirror*) Well, here I go . . . to run the gauntlet.

(*She starts out, followed by* MARGOT.)

DUSSEL

(*As she appears—sarcastic*)

Thank you so much.

(DUSSEL *goes into his room.* ANNE *goes toward* PETER'S *room, passing* MRS. VAN DAAN *and her parents at the center table.*)

MRS. VAN DAAN

My God, look at her! (ANNE *pays no attention. She knocks at* PETER'S *door*) I don't know what good it is to have a son. I never see him. He wouldn't care if I killed myself. (PETER *opens the door and stands aside for* ANNE *to come in*) Just a minute, Anne. (*She goes to them at the door*) I'd like to say a few words to my son. Do you mind? (PETER *and* ANNE *stand waiting*) Peter, I don't want you staying up till all hours tonight. You've got to have your sleep. You're a growing boy. You hear?

MRS. FRANK

Anne won't stay late. She's going to bed promptly at nine. Aren't you, Anne?

ANNE

Yes, Mother . . . (*To* MRS. VAN DAAN) May we go now?

MRS. VAN DAAN

Are you asking me? I didn't know I had anything to say about it.

MRS. FRANK

Listen for the chimes, Anne dear.
(*The two young people go off into* PETER's *room, shutting the door after them.*)

MRS. VAN DAAN

(*To* MRS. FRANK)

In my day it was the boys who called on the girls. Not the girls on the boys.

MRS. FRANK

You know how young people like to feel that they have secrets. Peter's room is the only place where they can talk.

MRS. VAN DAAN

Talk! That's not what they called it when I was young.

(MRS. VAN DAAN *goes off to the bathroom.* MARGOT *settles down to read her book.* MR. FRANK *puts his papers away and brings a chess game to the center table. He and* MRS. FRANK *start to play. In* PETER's *room,* ANNE *speaks to* PETER, *indignant, humiliated.*)

ANNE

Aren't they awful? Aren't they impossible? Treating us as if we were still in the nursery.

(*She sits on the cot.* PETER *gets a bottle of pop and two glasses.*)

PETER

Don't let it bother you. It doesn't bother me.

ANNE

I suppose you can't really blame them . . . they think back to what *they* were like at our age. They don't realize how much more advanced we are . . . When you think what wonderful discussions we've had! . . . Oh, I forgot. I was going to bring you some more pictures.

PETER

Oh, these are fine, thanks.

ANNE

Don't you want some more? Miep just brought me some new ones.

PETER

Maybe later.

(*He gives her a glass of pop and, taking some for himself, sits down facing her.*)

ANNE

(*Looking up at one of the photographs*)

I remember when I got that . . . I won it. I bet Jopie that I could eat five ice-cream cones. We'd all been playing ping-pong . . . We used to have heavenly times . . . we'd finish up with ice cream at the Delphi, or the Oasis, where Jews were allowed . . . there'd always be a lot of boys . . . we'd laugh and joke . . . I'd like to go back to it for a few days or a week. But after that I know I'd be bored to death. I think more seriously about life now. I want to be a journalist . . . or something. I love to write. What do you want to do?

PETER

I thought I might go off some place . . . work on a farm or something . . . some job that doesn't take much brains.

ANNE

You shouldn't talk that way. You've got the most awful inferiority complex.

PETER

I know I'm not smart.

ANNE

That isn't true. You're much better than I am in dozens of things . . . arithmetic and algebra and . . . well, you're a million times better than I am in algebra. (*With sudden direct-*

ness) You like Margot, don't you? Right from the start you liked her, liked her much better than me.

PETER

(*Uncomfortably*)

Oh, I don't know.

(*In the main room* MRS. VAN DAAN *comes from the bathroom and goes over to the sink, polishing a coffee pot.*)

ANNE

It's all right. Everyone feels that way. Margot's so good. She's sweet and bright and beautiful and I'm not.

PETER

I wouldn't say that.

ANNE

Oh, no, I'm not. I know that. I know quite well that I'm not a beauty. I never have been and never shall be.

PETER

I don't agree at all. I think you're pretty.

ANNE

That's not true!

PETER

And another thing. You've changed . . . from at first, I mean.

ANNE

I have?

PETER

I used to think you were awful noisy.

ANNE

And what do you think now, Peter? How have I changed?

PETER

Well . . . er . . . you're . . . quieter.
(*In his room* DUSSEL *takes his pajamas and toilet articles and goes into the bathroom to change.*)

ANNE

I'm glad you don't just hate me.

PETER

I never said that.

ANNE

I bet when you get out of here you'll never think of me again.

PETER

That's crazy.

ANNE

When you get back with all of your friends, you're going to say . . . now what did I ever see in that Mrs. Quack Quack.

PETER

I haven't got any friends.

ANNE

Oh, Peter, of course you have. Everyone has friends.

PETER

Not me. I don't want any. I get along all right without them.

ANNE

Does that mean you can get along without me? I think of myself as your friend.

PETER

No. If they were all like you, it'd be different.
(*He takes the glasses and the bottle and puts them away. There is a second's silence and then* ANNE *speaks, hesitantly, shyly.*)

ANNE

Peter, did you ever kiss a girl?

PETER

Yes. Once.

ANNE
(*To cover her feelings*)
That picture's crooked. (PETER *goes over, straightening the photograph.*) Was she pretty?

PETER

Huh?

ANNE

The girl that you kissed.

PETER

I don't know. I was blindfolded. (*He comes back and sits down again*) It was at a party. One of those kissing games.

ANNE

(Relieved)

Oh. I don't suppose that really counts, does it?

PETER

It didn't with me.

ANNE

I've been kissed twice. Once a man I'd never seen before kissed me on the cheek when he picked me up off the ice and I was crying. And the other was Mr. Koophuis, a friend of Father's who kissed my hand. You wouldn't say those counted, would you?

PETER

I wouldn't say so.

ANNE

I know almost for certain that Margot would never kiss any-one unless she was engaged to them. And I'm sure too that Mother never touched a man before Pim. But I don't know . . . things are so different now . . . What do you think? Do you think a girl shouldn't kiss anyone except if she's engaged or something? It's so hard to try to think what to do, when here we are with the whole world falling around our ears and you think . . . well . . . you don't know what's going to happen tomorrow and . . . What do you think?

PETER

I suppose it'd depend on the girl. Some girls, anything they do's wrong. But others . . . well . . . it wouldn't necessarily be wrong with them. (*The carillon starts to strike nine o'clock*) I've always thought that when two people . . .

ANNE

Nine o'clock. I have to go.

PETER

That's right.

ANNE

(*Without moving*)

Good night.
(*There is a second's pause, then* PETER *gets up and moves toward the door.*)

PETER

You won't let them stop you coming?

ANNE

No. (*She rises and starts for the door*) Sometime I might bring my diary. There are so many things in it that I want to talk over with you. There's a lot about you.

PETER

What kind of thing?

ANNE

I wouldn't want you to see some of it. I thought you were a nothing, just the way you thought about me.

PETER

Did you change your mind, the way I changed my mind about you?

ANNE

Well . . . You'll see . . .

(For a second ANNE *stands looking up at* PETER, *longing for him to kiss her. As he makes no move she turns away. Then suddenly* PETER *grabs her awkwardly in his arms, kissing her on the cheek.* ANNE *walks out dazed. She stands for a minute, her back to the people in the main room. As she regains her poise she goes to her mother and father and* MARGOT, *silently kissing them. They murmur their good nights to her. As she is about to open her bedroom door, she catches sight of* MRS. VAN DAAN. *She goes quickly to her, taking her face in her hands and kissing her first on one cheek and then on the other. Then she hurries off into her room.* MRS. VAN DAAN *looks after her, and then looks over at* PETER's *room. Her suspicions are confirmed.)*

MRS. VAN DAAN

(She knows)

Ah hah!

(The lights dim out. The curtain falls on the scene. In the darkness ANNE's VOICE *comes faintly at first and then with growing strength.)*

ANNE'S VOICE

By this time we all know each other so well that if anyone starts to tell a story, the rest can finish it for him. We're having

THE DIARY OF ANNE FRANK

to cut down still further on our meals. What makes it worse, the rats have been at work again. They've carried off some of our precious food. Even Mr. Dussel wishes now that Mouschi was here. Thursday, the twentieth of April, nineteen forty-four. Invasion fever is mounting every day. Miep tells us that people outside talk of nothing else. For myself, life has become much more pleasant. I often go to Peter's room after supper. Oh, don't think I'm in love, because I'm not. But it does make life more bearable to have someone with whom you can exchange views. No more tonight. P.S. . . . I must be honest. I must confess that I actually live for the next meeting. Is there anything lovelier than to sit under the skylight and feel the sun on your cheeks and have a darling boy in your arms? I admit now that I'm glad the Van Daans had a son and not a daughter. I've outgrown another dress. That's the third. I'm having to wear Margot's clothes after all. I'm working hard on my French and am now reading *La Belle Nivernaise*.

(*As she is saying the last lines—the curtain rises on the scene. The lights dim on, as* ANNE'S VOICE *fades out.*)

SCENE III

It is night, a few weeks later. Everyone is in bed. There is complete quiet. In the VAN DAANS' *room a match flares up for a moment and then is quickly put out.* MR. VAN DAAN, *in bare feet, dressed in underwear and trousers, is dimly seen coming stealthily down the stairs and into the main room, where* MR. *and* MRS. FRANK *and* MARGOT *are sleeping. He goes to the food safe and again lights a match. Then he cautiously opens the safe, taking out a half-loaf of bread. As he closes the safe, it creaks. He stands rigid.* MRS. FRANK *sits up in bed. She sees him.*

MRS. FRANK
(Screaming)
Otto! Otto! *Komme schnell!* [1]
(The rest of the people wake, hurriedly getting up.)

MR. FRANK
Was ist los? Was ist passiert? [2]
(DUSSEL, *followed by* ANNE, *comes from his room.*)

MRS. FRANK
(As she rushes over to MR. VAN DAAN*)*
Er stiehlt das Essen! [3]

DUSSEL
(Grabbing MR. VAN DAAN*)*
You! You! Give me that.

MRS. VAN DAAN
(Coming down the stairs)
Putti . . . Putti . . . what is it?

---

[1]*Komme schnell:* "Come quick."
[2]*Was ist los? Was ist passiert?:* "What's wrong? What's going on?"
[3]*Er stiehlt das Essen:* "He's stealing food."

DUSSEL

(*His hands on* VAN DAAN'S *neck*)

You dirty thief . . . stealing food . . . you good-for-nothing . . .

MR. FRANK

Mr. Dussel! For God's sake! Help me, Peter!

(PETER *comes over, trying, with* MR. FRANK, *to separate the two struggling men.*)

PETER

Let him go! Let go!

(DUSSEL *drops* MR. VAN DAAN, *pushing him away. He shows them the end of a loaf of bread that he has taken from* VAN DAAN.)

DUSSEL

You greedy, selfish . . . !

(MARGOT *turns on the lights.*)

MRS. VAN DAAN

Putti . . . what is it?

(*All of* MRS. FRANK'S *gentleness, her self-control, is gone. She is outraged, in a frenzy of indignation.*)

MRS. FRANK

The bread! He was stealing the bread!

DUSSEL

It was you, and all the time we thought it was the rats!

MR. FRANK

Mr. Van Daan, how could you!

MR. VAN DAAN

I'm hungry.

MRS. FRANK

We're all of us hungry! I see the children getting thinner and thinner. Your own son Peter . . . I've heard him moan in his sleep, he's so hungry. And you come in the night and steal food that should go to them . . . to the children!

MRS. VAN DAAN

(*Going to* MR. VAN DAAN *protectively*)

He needs more food than the rest of us. He's used to more. He's a big man.

(MR. VAN DAAN *breaks away, going over and sitting on the couch.*)

MRS. FRANK

(*Turning on* MRS. VAN DAAN)

And you . . . you're worse than he is! You're a mother, and yet you sacrifice your child to this man . . . this . . . this . . .

MR. FRANK

Edith! Edith!

(MARGOT *picks up the pink woolen stole, putting it over her mother's shoulders.*)

MRS. FRANK

(*Paying no attention, going on to* MRS. VAN DAAN)

Don't think I haven't seen you! Always saving the choicest bits for him! I've watched you day after day and I've held my tongue. But not any longer! Not after this! Now I want him to go! I want him to get out of here!

MR. FRANK

Edith!

MR. VAN DAAN

Together

Get out of here?

MRS. VAN DAAN

What do you mean?

MRS. FRANK

Just that! Take your things and get out!

MR. FRANK

(*To* MRS. FRANK)

You're speaking in anger. You cannot mean what you are saying.

MRS. FRANK

I mean exactly that!

(MRS. VAN DAAN *takes a cover from the* FRANKS' *bed, pulling it about her.*)

MR. FRANK

For two long years we have lived here, side by side. We have respected each other's rights . . . we have managed to live in peace. Are we now going to throw it all away? I know this will never happen again, will it, Mr. Van Daan?

MR. VAN DAAN

No. No.

MRS. FRANK

He steals once! He'll steal again!

(MR. VAN DAAN, *holding his stomach, starts for the bathroom.* ANNE *puts her arms around him, helping him up the step.*)

MR. FRANK

Edith, please. Let us be calm. We'll all go to our rooms . . . and afterwards we'll sit down quietly and talk this out . . . we'll find some way . . .

MRS. FRANK

No! No! No more talk! I want them to leave!

MRS. VAN DAAN

You'd put us out, on the streets?

MRS. FRANK

There are other hiding places.

MRS. VAN DAAN

A cellar . . . a closet. I know. And we have no money left even to pay for that.

MRS. FRANK

I'll give you money. Out of my own pocket I'll give it gladly.

(*She gets her purse from a shelf and comes back with it.*)

MRS. VAN DAAN

Mr. Frank, you told Putti you'd never forget what he'd done for you when you came to Amsterdam. You said you could never repay him, that you . . .

MRS. FRANK

(*Counting out money*)

If my husband had any obligation to you, he's paid it, over and over.

MR. FRANK

Edith, I've never seen you like this before. I don't know you.

MRS. FRANK

I should have spoken out long ago.

DUSSEL

You can't be nice to some people.

MRS. VAN DAAN

(*Turning on* DUSSEL)

There would have been plenty for all of us, if *you* hadn't come in here!

MR. FRANK

We don't need the Nazis to destroy us. We're destroying our-selves.

(*He sits down, with his head in his hands.* MRS. FRANK *goes to* MRS. VAN DAAN.)

MRS. FRANK

(*Giving* MRS. VAN DAAN *some money*)

Give this to Miep. She'll find you a place.

ANNE

Mother, you're not putting *Peter* out. Peter hasn't done any-thing.

MRS. FRANK

He'll stay, of course. When I say I must protect the children, I mean Peter too.

(PETER *rises from the steps where he has been sitting.*)

PETER

I'd have to go if Father goes.

(MR. VAN DAAN *comes from the bathroom.* MRS. VAN DAAN

hurries to him and takes him to the couch. Then she gets water from the sink to bathe his face.)

MRS. FRANK

(*While this is going on*)

He's no father to you . . . that man! He doesn't know what it is to be a father!

PETER

(*Starting for his room*)

I wouldn't feel right. I couldn't stay.

MRS. FRANK

Very well, then. I'm sorry.

ANNE

(*Rushing over to* PETER)

No, Peter! No! (PETER *goes into his room, closing the door after him.* ANNE *turns back to her mother, crying*) I don't care about the food. They can have mine! I don't want it! Only don't send them away. It'll be daylight soon. They'll be caught . . .

MARGOT

(*Putting her arms comfortingly around* ANNE)

Please, Mother!

MRS. FRANK

They're not going now. They'll stay here until Miep finds them a place. (*To* MRS. VAN DAAN) But one thing I insist on! He must never come down here again! He must never come to this room where the food is stored! We'll divide what we have . . . an equal share for each! (DUSSEL *hurries over to get a sack of potatoes from the food safe.* MRS. FRANK *goes on, to* MRS. VAN DAAN) You can cook it here and take it up to him.

(DUSSEL *brings the sack of potatoes back to the center table.*)

MARGOT

Oh, no. No. We haven't sunk so far that we're going to fight over a handful of rotten potatoes.

DUSSEL

(*Dividing the potatoes into piles*)
Mrs. Frank, Mr. Frank, Margot, Anne, Peter, Mrs. Van Daan, Mr. Van Daan, myself . . . Mrs. Frank . . .
(*The buzzer sounds in* MIEP'S *signal.*)

MR. FRANK

It's Miep!
(*He hurries over, getting his overcoat and putting it on.*)

MARGOT

At this hour?

MRS. FRANK

It is trouble.

MR. FRANK

(*As he starts down to unbolt the door*)
I beg you, don't let her see a thing like this!

MR. DUSSEL

(*Counting without stopping*)
. . . Anne, Peter, Mrs. Van Daan, Mr. Van Daan, myself . . .

MARGOT

(*To* DUSSEL)

Stop it! Stop it!

DUSSEL

. . . Mr. Frank, Margot, Anne, Peter, Mrs. Van Daan, Mr. Van Daan, myself, Mrs. Frank . . .

MRS. VAN DAAN

You're keeping the big ones for yourself! All the big ones . . . Look at the size of that! . . . And that! . . .

(DUSSEL *continues on with his dividing.* PETER, *with his shirt and trousers on, comes from his room.*)

MARGOT

Stop it! Stop it!

(*We hear* MIEP's *excited voice speaking to* MR. FRANK *below.*)

MIEP

Mr. Frank . . . the most wonderful news! . . . The invasion has begun!

MR. FRANK

Go on, tell them! Tell them!

(MIEP *comes running up the steps, ahead of* MR. FRANK. *She has a man's raincoat on over her nightclothes and a bunch of orange-colored flowers in her hand.*)

MIEP

Did you hear that, everybody? Did you hear what I said? The invasion has begun! The invasion!

(They all stare at MIEP, *unable to grasp what she is telling them.* PETER *is the first to recover his wits.)*

PETER

Where?

MRS. VAN DAAN

When? When, Miep?

MIEP

It began early this morning . . .
(As she talks on, the realization of what she has said begins to dawn on them. Everyone goes crazy. A wild demonstration takes place. MRS. FRANK *hugs* MR. VAN DAAN.)*

MRS. FRANK

Oh, Mr. Van Daan, did you hear that?
*(*DUSSEL *embraces* MRS. VAN DAAN. PETER *grabs a frying pan and parades around the room, beating on it, singing the Dutch National Anthem.* ANNE *and* MARGOT *follow him, singing, weaving in and out among the excited grownups.* MARGOT *breaks away to take the flowers from* MIEP *and distribute them to everyone. While this pandemonium is going on* MRS. FRANK *tries to make herself heard above the excitement.)*

MRS. FRANK
(To MIEP)

How do you know?

MIEP

The radio . . . The B.B.C.! They said they landed on the coast of Normandy!

PETER

The British?

MIEP

British, Americans, French, Dutch, Poles, Norwegians . . . all of them! More than four thousand ships! Churchill spoke, and General Eisenhower! D-Day they call it!

MR. FRANK

Thank God, it's come!

MRS. VAN DAAN

At last!

MIEP

(*Starting out*)

I'm going to tell Mr. Kraler. This'll be better than any blood transfusion.

MR. FRANK

(*Stopping her*)

What part of Normandy did they land, did they say?

MIEP

Normandy . . . that's all I know now . . . I'll be up the minute I hear some more!

(*She goes hurriedly out.*)

MR. FRANK

(*To* MRS. FRANK)

What did I tell you? What did I tell you?

(MRS. FRANK *indicates that he has forgotten to bolt the door after* MIEP. *He hurries down the steps.* MR. VAN DAAN, *sitting on the couch, suddenly breaks into a convulsive sob. Everybody looks at him, bewildered.)*

MRS. VAN DAAN

(Hurrying to him)

Putti! Putti! What is it? What happened?

MR. VAN DAAN

Please. I'm so ashamed.

(MR. FRANK comes back up the steps.)

DUSSEL

Oh, for God's sake!

MRS. VAN DAAN

Don't, Putti.

MARGOT

It doesn't matter now!

MR. FRANK

(Going to MR. VAN DAAN)

Didn't you hear what Miep said? The invasion has come! We're going to be liberated! This is a time to celebrate!

(He embraces MRS. FRANK and then hurries to the cupboard and gets the cognac and a glass.)

MR. VAN DAAN

To steal bread from children!

MRS. FRANK

We've all done things that we're ashamed of.

ANNE

Look at me, the way I've treated Mother . . . so mean and horrid to her.

MRS. FRANK

No, Anneke, no.
(ANNE *runs to her mother, putting her arms around her.*)

ANNE

Oh, Mother, I was. I was awful.

MR. VAN DAAN

Not like me. No one is as bad as me!

DUSSEL

(*To* MR. VAN DAAN)
Stop it now! Let's be happy!

MR. FRANK

(*Giving* MR. VAN DAAN *a glass of cognac*)
Here! Here! *Schnapps! Locheim!*[4]
(VAN DAAN *takes the cognac. They all watch him. He gives
them a feeble smile.* ANNE *puts up her fingers in a V-for-
Victory sign. As* VAN DAAN *gives an answering V-sign,
they are startled to hear a loud sob from behind them. It
is* MRS. FRANK, *stricken with remorse. She is sitting on the
other side of the room.*)

MRS. FRANK

(*Through her sobs*)
When I think of the terrible things I said . . .
(MR. FRANK, ANNE *and* MARGOT *hurry to her, trying to
comfort her.* MR. VAN DAAN *brings her his glass of cognac.*)

MR. VAN DAAN

No! No! You were right!

---

[4]*Schnapps! Locheim!:* "A drink! To life!" (traditional Jewish toast).

MRS. FRANK

That I should speak that way to you! . . . Our friends! . . . Our guests!

(*She starts to cry again.*)

DUSSEL

Stop it, you're spoiling the whole invasion!

(*As they are comforting her, the lights dim out. The curtain falls.*)

ANNE'S VOICE

(*Faintly at first and then with growing strength*)

We're all in much better spirits these days. There's still excellent news of the invasion. The best part about it is that I have a feeling that friends are coming. Who knows? Maybe I'll be back in school by fall. Ha, ha! The joke is on us! The warehouse man doesn't know a thing and we are paying him all that money! . . . Wednesday, the second of July, nineteen forty-four. The invasion seems temporarily to be bogged down. Mr. Kraler has to have an operation, which looks bad. The Gestapo have found the radio that was stolen. Mr. Dussel says they'll trace it back and back to the thief, and then, it's just a matter of time till they get to us. Everyone is low. Even poor Pim can't raise their spirits. I have often been downcast myself . . . but never in despair. I can shake off everything if I write. But . . . and that is the great question . . . will I ever be able to write well? I want to so much. I want to go on living even after my death. Another birthday has gone by, so now I am fifteen. Already I know what I want. I have a goal, an opinion.

(*As this is being said—the curtain rises on the scene, the lights dim on, and ANNE'S VOICE fades out.*)

SCENE IV

*It is an afternoon a few weeks later . . . Everyone but Margot
is in the main room. There is a sense of great tension.*

Both MRS. FRANK *and* MR. VAN DAAN *are nervously pacing back
and forth,* DUSSEL *is standing at the window, looking down
fixedly at the street below.* PETER *is at the center table, trying to
do his lessons.* ANNE *sits opposite him, writing in her diary.* MRS.
VAN DAAN *is seated on the couch, her eyes on* MR. FRANK *as he sits
reading.*

*The sound of a telephone ringing comes from the office below.
They all are rigid, listening tensely.* MR. DUSSEL *rushes down to*
MR. FRANK.

DUSSEL

There it goes again, the telephone! Mr. Frank, do you hear?

MR. FRANK
(Quietly)

Yes. I hear.

DUSSEL

(Pleading, insistent)

But this is the third time, Mr. Frank! The third time in quick
succession! It's a signal! I tell you it's Miep, trying to get us! For
some reason she can't come to us and she's trying to warn us of
something!

MR. FRANK

Please. Please.

MR. VAN DAAN

(*To* DUSSEL)

You're wasting your breath.

DUSSEL

Something has happened, Mr. Frank. For three days now Miep hasn't been to see us! And today not a man has come to work. There hasn't been a sound in the building!

MRS. FRANK

Perhaps it's Sunday. We may have lost track of the days.

MR. VAN DAAN

(*To* ANNE)

You with the diary there. What day is it?

DUSSEL

(*Going to* MRS. FRANK)

I don't lose track of the days! I know exactly what day it is! It's Friday, the fourth of August. Friday, and not a man at work. (*He rushes back to* MR. FRANK, *pleading with him, almost in tears*) I tell you Mr. Kraler's dead. That's the only explanation. He's dead and they've closed down the building, and Miep's trying to tell us!

MR. FRANK

She'd never telephone us.

DUSSEL

(*Frantic*)

Mr. Frank, answer that! I beg you, answer it!

MR. FRANK

No.

MR. VAN DAAN

Just pick it up and listen. You don't have to speak. Just listen and see if it's Miep.

DUSSEL

(*Speaking at the same time*)

For God's sake . . . I ask you.

MR. FRANK

No. I've told you, no. I'll do nothing that might let anyone know we're in the building.

PETER

Mr. Frank's right.

MR. VAN DAAN

There's no need to tell us what side you're on.

MR. FRANK

If we wait patiently, quietly, I believe that help will come.

(*There is silence for a minute as they all listen to the telephone ringing.*)

DUSSEL

I'm going down. (*He rushes down the steps.* MR. FRANK *tries ineffectually to hold him.* DUSSEL *runs to the lower door, unbolting it. The telephone stops ringing.* DUSSEL *bolts the door and comes slowly back up the steps.*) Too late. (MR. FRANK *goes to* MARGOT *in* ANNE'S *bedroom.*)

MR. VAN DAAN

So we just wait here until we die.

MRS. VAN DAAN

(*Hysterically*)
I can't stand it! I'll kill myself! I'll kill myself!

MR. VAN DAAN

For God's sake, stop it!
(*In the distance, a German military band is heard playing a Viennese waltz.*)

MRS. VAN DAAN

I think you'd be glad if I did! I think you want me to die!

MR. VAN DAAN

Whose fault is it we're here? (MRS. VAN DAAN *starts for her room. He follows, talking at her*) We could've been safe somewhere . . . in America or Switzerland. But no! No! You wouldn't leave when I wanted to. You couldn't leave your things. You couldn't leave your precious furniture.

MRS. VAN DAAN

Don't touch me!
(*She hurries up the stairs, followed by* MR. VAN DAAN. PETER, *unable to bear it, goes to his room.* ANNE *looks after him, deeply concerned.* DUSSEL *returns to his post at the window.* MR. FRANK *comes back into the main room and takes a book, trying to read.* MRS. FRANK *sits near the sink, starting to peel some potatoes.* ANNE *quietly goes to* PETER's *room, closing the door after her.* PETER *is lying face*

down on the cot. ANNE *leans over him, holding him in her arms, trying to bring him out of his despair.*)

ANNE

Look, Peter, the sky. (*She looks up through the skylight*) What a lovely, lovely day! Aren't the clouds beautiful? You know what I do when it seems as if I couldn't stand being cooped up for one more minute? I *think* myself out. I think myself on a walk in the park where I used to go with Pim. Where the jonquils and the crocus and the violets grow down the slopes. You know the most wonderful part about *thinking* yourself out? You can have it any way you like. You can have roses and violets and chrysanthemums all blooming at the same time . . . It's funny . . . I used to take it all for granted . . . and now I've gone crazy about everything to do with nature. Haven't you?

PETER

I've just gone crazy. I think if something doesn't happen soon . . . if we don't get out of here . . . I can't stand much more of it!

ANNE

(*Softly*)

I wish you had a religion, Peter.

PETER

No, thanks! Not me!

ANNE

Oh, I don't mean you have to be Orthodox[5] . . . or believe in heaven and hell and purgatory and things . . . I just mean

---

[5]*Orthodox:* the most strictly observant branch of Judaism.

some religion . . . it doesn't matter what. Just to believe in some-thing! When I think of all that's out there . . . the trees . . . and flowers . . . and seagulls . . . when I think of the dearness of you, Peter . . . and the goodness of the people we know . . . Mr. Kraler, Miep, Dirk, the vegetable man, all risking their lives for us every day . . . When I think of these good things, I'm not afraid any more . . . I find myself, and God, and I . . .

(PETER *interrupts, getting up and walking away.*)

PETER

That's fine! But when I begin to think, I get mad! Look at us, hiding out for two years. Not able to move! Caught here like . . . waiting for them to come and get us . . . and all for what?

ANNE

We're not the only people that've had to suffer. There've al-ways been people that've had to . . . sometimes one race . . . sometimes another . . . and yet . . .

PETER

That doesn't make me feel any better!

ANNE

(*Going to him*)

I know it's terrible, trying to have any faith . . . when people are doing such horrible . . . But you know what I sometimes think? I think the world may be going through a phase, the way I was with Mother. It'll pass, maybe not for hundreds of years, but some day . . . I still believe, in spite of everything, that people are really good at heart.

PETER

I want to see something now . . . Not a thousand years from now!

(*He goes over, sitting down again on the cot.*)

ANNE

But, Peter, if you'd only look at it as part of a great pattern . . . that we're just a little minute in the life . . . (*She breaks off*) Listen to us, going at each other like a couple of stupid grownups! Look at the sky now. Isn't it lovely? (*She holds out her hand to him.* PETER *takes it and rises, standing with her at the window looking out, his arms around her*) Some day, when we're outside again, I'm going to . . .

(*She breaks off as she hears the sound of a car, its brakes squealing as it comes to a sudden stop. The people in the other rooms also become aware of the sound. They listen tensely. Another car roars up to a screeching stop.* ANNE *and* PETER *come from* PETER's *room.* MR. *and* MRS. VAN DAAN *creep down the stairs.* DUSSEL *comes out from his room. Everyone is listening, hardly breathing. A doorbell clangs again and again in the building below.* MR. FRANK *starts quietly down the steps to the door.* DUSSEL *and* PETER *follow him. The others stand rigid, waiting, terrified.*

In a few seconds DUSSEL *comes stumbling back up the steps. He shakes off* PETER's *help and goes to his room.* MR. FRANK *bolts the door below, and comes slowly back up the steps. Their eyes are all on him as he stands there for a minute. They realize that what they feared has happened.*

MRS. VAN DAAN *starts to whimper.* MR. VAN DAAN *puts her gently in a chair, and then hurries off up the stairs to their room to collect their things.* PETER *goes to comfort his mother. There is a sound of violent pounding on a door below.*)

MR. FRANK
(*Quietly*)

For the past two years we have lived in fear. Now we can live in hope.

(*The pounding below becomes more insistent. There are muffled sounds of voices, shouting commands.*)

MEN'S VOICES

Auf machen! Da drinnen! Auf machen! Schnell! Schnell! Schnell! etc., etc.[6]

(*The street door below is forced open. We hear the heavy tread of footsteps coming up.* MR. FRANK *gets two school bags from the shelves, and gives one to* ANNE *and the other to* MARGOT. *He goes to get a bag for* MRS. FRANK. *The sound of feet coming up grows louder.* PETER *comes to* ANNE, *kissing her good-bye, then he goes to his room to collect his things. The buzzer of their door starts to ring.* MR. FRANK *brings* MRS. FRANK *a bag. They stand together, waiting. We hear the thud of gun butts on the door, trying to break it down.*

ANNE *stands, holding her school satchel, looking over at her father and mother with a soft, reassuring smile. She is no longer a child, but a woman with courage to meet whatever lies ahead.*

---

[6]*Auf machen...Schnell:* "Open up! You in there! Quick! Quick! Quick!"

The lights dim out. The curtain falls on the scene. We hear a mighty crash as the door is shattered. After a second ANNE'S *voice is heard.*)

ANNE'S VOICE

And so it seems our stay here is over. They are waiting for us now. They've allowed us five minutes to get our things. We can each take a bag and whatever it will hold of clothing. Nothing else. So, dear Diary, that means I must leave you behind. Goodbye for a while. P.S. Please, please, Miep, or Mr. Kraler, or anyone else. If you should find this diary, will you please keep it safe for me, because some day I hope . . .

(*Her voice stops abruptly. There is silence. After a second the curtain rises.*)

Scene V

It is again the afternoon in November, 1945. The rooms are as we saw them in the first scene. MR. KRALER *has joined* MIEP *and* MR. FRANK. *There are coffee cups on the table. We see a great change in* MR. FRANK. *He is calm now. His bitterness is gone. He slowly turns a few pages of the diary. They are blank.*

MR. FRANK

No more.
>   (*He closes the diary and puts it down on the couch beside him.*)

MIEP

I'd gone to the country to find food. When I got back the block was surrounded by police . . .

MR. KRALER

We made it our business to learn how they knew. It was the thief . . . the thief who told them.
>   (MIEP *goes up to the gas burner, bringing back a pot of coffee.*)

MR. FRANK

(*After a pause*)

It seems strange to say this, that anyone could be happy in a concentration camp. But Anne was happy in the camp in Holland where they first took us. After two years of being shut up in these rooms, she could be out . . . out in the sunshine and the fresh air that she loved.

MIEP

(*Offering the coffee to* MR. FRANK)

A little more?

MR. FRANK

(*Holding out his cup to her*)

The news of the war was good. The British and Americans were sweeping through France. We felt sure that they would get to us in time. In September we were told that we were to be shipped to Poland . . . The men to one camp. The women to another. I was sent to Auschwitz. They went to Belsen. In January we were freed, the few of us who were left. The war wasn't yet over, so it took us a long time to get home. We'd be sent here and there behind the lines where we'd be safe. Each time our train would stop . . . at a siding, or a crossing . . . we'd all get out and go from group to group . . . Where were you? Were you at Belsen? At Buchenwald? At Mauthausen? Is it possible that you knew my wife? Did you ever see my husband? My son? My daughter? That's how I found out about my wife's death . . . of Margot, the Van Daans . . . Dussel. But Anne . . . I still hoped . . . Yesterday I went to Rotterdam. I'd heard of a woman there . . . She'd been in Belsen with Anne . . . I know now.

(*He picks up the diary again, and turns the pages back to find a certain passage. As he finds it we hear* ANNE'S VOICE.)

ANNE'S VOICE

In spite of everything, I still believe that people are really good at heart.

(MR. FRANK *slowly closes the diary.*)

MR. FRANK

She puts me to shame.
(*They are silent.*)

The Curtain Falls

Discussion

1. What do you think Mr. Frank means when he says of Anne, "She puts me to shame"?

2. In spite of the danger and fear Anne lived with, she remained a fairly typical thirteen-year-old. How do you think it was possible for her to remain normal under those circumstances?

3. The other occupants of the attic constantly reminded Anne that she was not nice and quiet like her sister Margot. Why were they unwilling to accept Anne as she was?

4. Anne said she was afraid to show the "sweeter, nicer side" of her character because people might laugh at her if she were serious. Do you think she was right? Why?

5. All the characters display some form of heroism. Think about the characters and what they did. Based on all their actions, how would you define *heroism?*

Excerpts from
Anne Frank:
The Diary of
a Young Girl

Introduction

Anne Frank made the first entry in her diary on June 14, 1942, and the last on August 1, 1944. During those two years, Anne recorded her innermost thoughts and her observations of life in the "Secret Annex."

The impact that Anne's diary has had on the world probably cannot be measured. At first Mr. Frank had copies of the diary privately circulated as a memorial to his family. Eventually it was formally published and has been translated into more than thirty languages. Over thirty million copies of the diary have been sold.

The excerpts that follow allow you to experience, for a brief moment, the constant pressure that Anne, her family, and their friends had to endure during their enforced concealment.

Excerpts from
Anne Frank:
The Diary
of a Young Girl

by Anne Frank

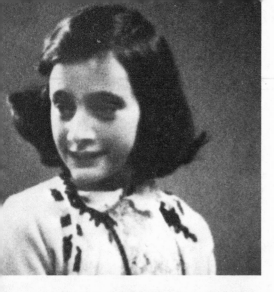

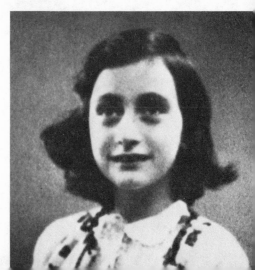

INTRODUCTION

This is a remarkable book. Written by a young girl—and the young are not afraid of telling the truth—it is one of the wisest and most moving commentaries on war and its impact on human beings that I have ever read. Anne Frank's account of the changes wrought upon eight people hiding out from the Nazis for two years during the occupation of Holland, living in constant fear and isolation, imprisoned not only by the terrible outward circumstances of war but inwardly by themselves, made me intimately and shockingly aware of war's greatest evil—the degradation of the human spirit.

At the same time, Anne's diary makes poignantly clear the ultimate shining nobility of that spirit. Despite the horror and the humiliation of their daily lives, these people never gave up. Anne herself—and, most of all, it is her portrait which emerges so vividly and so appealingly from this book—matured very rapidly in these two years, the crucial years from thirteen to fifteen in which change is so swift and so difficult for every young girl. Sustained by her warmth and her wit, her intelligence and the rich resources of her inner life, Anne wrote and thought much of the time about things which very sensitive and talented adolescents without the threat of death will write—her relations with her parents, her developing self-awareness, the problems of growing up.

These are the thoughts and expression of a young girl living under extraordinary conditions, and for this reason her diary tells us much about ourselves and about our own children. And for this reason, too, I felt how close we all are to Anne's experience, how very much involved we are in her short life and in the entire world.

Anne's diary is an appropriate monument to her fine spirit and to the spirits of those who have worked and are working still for peace. Reading it is a rich and rewarding experience.

—Eleanor Roosevelt

Ik zal hoop ik aan jou alles kunnen toevertrouwen, zoals ik het nog aan niemand gekund heb, en ik hoop dat je me een grote steun zult zijn.

Anne Frank. 12 Juni 1942.

I hope I shall be able to confide in you completely, as I have never been able to do in anyone before, and I hope that you will be a great support and comfort to me.

—Anne Frank

Saturday, 20 June, 1942

I haven't written for a few days, because I wanted first of all to think about my diary. It's an odd idea for someone like me to keep a diary; not only because I have never done so before, but because it seems to me that neither I—nor for that matter anyone else—will be interested in the unbosomings of a thirteen-year-old schoolgirl. Still, what does that matter? I want to write, but more than that, I want to bring out all kinds of things that lie buried deep in my heart.

There is a saying that "paper is more patient than man"; it came back to me on one of my slightly melancholy days, while I sat chin in hand, feeling too bored and limp even to make up my mind whether to go out or stay at home. Yes, there is no doubt that paper is patient and as I don't intend to show this cardboard-covered notebook, bearing the proud name of "diary," to anyone, unless I find a real friend, boy or girl, probably nobody cares. And now I come to the root of the matter, the reason for my starting a diary: it is that I have no such real friend.

Let me put it more clearly, since no one will believe that a girl of thirteen feels herself quite alone in the world, nor is it so. I have darling parents and a sister of sixteen. I know about thirty people whom one might call friends—I have strings of boy friends, anxious to catch a glimpse of me and who, failing that, peep at me through mirrors in class. I have relations, aunts and uncles, who are darlings too, a good home, no—I don't seem to lack anything. But it's the same with all my friends, just fun and joking, nothing more. I can never bring myself to talk of anything outside the common round. We don't seem to be able to get any closer, that is the root of the trouble. Perhaps I lack confidence, but anyway, there it is, a stubborn fact and I don't seem to be able to do anything about it.

Hence, this diary. In order to enhance in my mind's eye the picture of the friend for whom I have waited so long, I don't want to set down a series of bald facts in a diary like most people do, but I want this diary itself to be my friend, and I shall call my friend Kitty. No one will grasp what I'm talking about if I begin my letters to Kitty just out of the blue, so albeit unwillingly, I will start by sketching in brief the story of my life.

My father was thirty-six when he married my mother, who was then twenty-five. My sister Margot was born in 1926 in Frankfort-on-Main, I followed on June 12, 1929, and, as we are Jewish, we emigrated to Holland in 1933, where my father was appointed Managing Director of Travies N.V. This firm is in close relationship with the firm of Kolen & Co. in the same building, of which my father is a partner.

The rest of our family, however, felt the full impact of Hitler's anti-Jewish laws, so life was filled with anxiety. In 1938 after the pogroms, my two uncles (my mother's brothers) escaped to the U.S.A. My old grandmother came to us, she was then seventy-three. After May 1940 good times rapidly fled: first the war, then the capitulation, followed by the arrival of the Germans, which is when the sufferings of us Jews really began. Anti-Jewish decrees followed each other in quick succession. Jews must wear a yellow star, Jews must hand in their bicycles, Jews are banned from trains and are forbidden to drive. Jews are only allowed to do their shopping between three and five o'clock and then only in shops which bear the placard "Jewish shop." Jews must be indoors by eight o'clock and cannot even sit in their own gardens after that hour. Jews are forbidden to visit theaters, cinemas, and other places of entertainment. Jews may not take part in public sports. Swimming baths, tennis courts, hockey fields, and other sports grounds are all prohibited to them. Jews may not visit Christians. Jews must go to Jewish schools, and many more restrictions of a similar kind.

So we could not do this and were forbidden to do that. But life went on in spite of it all. Jopie used to say to me, "You're scared to do anything, because it may be forbidden." Our freedom was strictly limited. Yet things were still bearable.

Granny died in January 1942; no one will ever know how much she is present in my thoughts and how much I love her still.

In 1934 I went to school at the Montessori Kindergarten and continued there. It was at the end of the school year, I was in form 6B, when I had to say good-by to Mrs. K. We both wept, it was very sad. In 1941 I went, with my sister Margot, to the Jewish Secondary School, she into the fourth form and I into the first.

So far everything is all right with the four of us and here I come to the present day.

Tuesday, 11 April, 1944

Dear Kitty,

My head throbs, I honestly don't know where to begin.

On Friday (Good Friday) we played Monopoly, Saturday afternoon too. These days passed quickly and uneventfully. On Sunday afternoon, on my invitation, Peter came to my room at half past four; at a quarter past five we went to the front attic, where we remained until six o'clock. There was a beautiful Mozart concert on the radio from six o'clock until a quarter past seven. I enjoyed it all very much, but especially the "Kleine Nachtmusik." I can hardly listen in the room because I'm always so inwardly stirred when I hear lovely music.

On Sunday evening Peter and I went to the front attic together and, in order to sit comfortably, we took with us a few divan cushions that we were able to lay our hands on. We seated ourselves on one packing case. Both the case and the cushions were very narrow, so we sat absolutely squashed together, learning against other cases. Mouschi kept us company too, so we weren't unchaperoned.

Suddenly, at a quarter to nine, Mr. Van Daan whistled and asked if we had one of Dussel's cushions. We both jumped up and went downstairs with cushion, cat, and Van Daan.

A lot of trouble arose out of this cushion, because Dussel was annoyed that we had one of his cushions, one that he used as a pillow. He was afraid that there might be fleas in it and made a great commotion about this beloved cushion! Peter and I put two hard brushes in his bed as a revenge. We had a good laugh over this little interlude!

Our fun didn't last long. At half past nine Peter knocked softly on the door and asked Daddy if he would just help him upstairs over a difficult English sentence. "That's a blind," I said to Margot, "anyone could see through that one!" I was right. They were in the act of breaking into the warehouse. Daddy, Van Daan, Dussel, and Peter were downstairs in a flash. Margot, Mummy, Mrs. Van Daan, and I stayed upstairs and waited.

Four frightened women just have to talk, so talk we did, until we heard a bang downstairs. After that all was quiet, the clock struck a quarter to ten. The color had vanished from our faces, we were still quiet, although we were afraid. Where could the men be? What was that bang? Would they be fighting the burglars? Ten o'clock, footsteps on the stairs: Daddy, white and nervous, entered, followed by Mr. Van Daan. "Lights out, creep upstairs, we expect the police in the house!"

There was no time to be frightened: the lights went out, I quickly grabbed a jacket, and we were upstairs. "What has happened? Tell us quickly!" There was no one to tell us, the men having disappeared downstairs again. Only at ten past ten did they reappear; two kept watch at Peter's open window, the door to the landing was closed, the swinging cupboard shut. We hung a jersey round the night light, and after that they told us:

Peter heard two loud bangs on the landing, ran downstairs, and saw there was a large plank out of the left half of the door. He dashed upstairs, warned the "Home Guard" of the family, and the four of them proceeded downstairs. When they entered the warehouse, the burglars were in the act of enlarging the hole. Without further thought Van Daan shouted: "Police!"

A few hurried steps outside, and the burglars had fled. In order to avoid the hole being noticed by the police, a plank was put against it, but a good hard kick from outside sent it flying to the ground. The men were perplexed at such impudence, and both Van Daan and Peter felt murder welling up within them; Van Daan beat on the ground with a chopper, and all was quiet again. Once more they wanted to put the plank in front of the hole. Disturbance! A married couple outside shone a torch through the opening, lighting up the whole warehouse. "Hell!" muttered one of the men, and now they switched over from their role of police to that of burglars. The four of them sneaked upstairs, Peter quickly opened the doors and windows of the kitchen and private office, flung the telephone onto the floor, and finally the four of them landed behind the swinging cupboard.

END OF PART ONE

The married couple with the torch would probably have warned the police: it was Sunday evening, Easter Sunday, no one at the office on Easter Monday, so none of us could budge until Tuesday morning. Think of it, waiting in such fear for two nights and a day! No one had anything to suggest, so we simply sat there in pitch-darkness, because Mrs. Van Daan in her fright had unintentionally turned the lamp right out; talked in whispers, and at every creak one heard "Sh! sh!"

It turned half past ten, eleven, but not a sound; Daddy and Van Daan joined us in turns. Then a quarter past eleven, a bustle and noise downstairs. Everyone's breath was audible, otherwise no one moved. Footsteps in the house, in the private office, kitchen, then . . . on our staircase. No one breathed audibly now, footsteps on our staircase, then a rattling of the swinging cupboard. This moment is indescribable. "Now we are lost!" I said, and could see us all being taken away by the Gestapo that very night. Twice they rattled at the cupboard, then there was nothing, the footsteps withdrew, we were saved so far. A shiver seemed to pass from one to another. I heard someone's teeth chattering, no one said a word.

There was not another sound in the house, but a light was burning on our landing, right in front of the cupboard. Could that be because it was a secret cupboard? Perhaps the police had forgotten the light? Would someone come back to put it out? Tongues loosened, there was no one in the house any longer, perhaps there was someone on guard outside. . . .

I prepared myself for the return of the police, then we'd have to say that we were in hiding; they would either be good Dutch people, then we'd be saved, or N.S.B.-ers,[1] then we'd have to bribe them!

"In that case, destroy the radio," sighed Mrs. Van Daan. "Yes, in the stove!" replied her husband. "If they find us, then let them find the radio as well!"

"Then they will find Anne's diary," added Daddy. "Burn them," suggested the most terrified member of the party. This, and when the police rattled the cupboard door, were my worst moments. "Not my diary; if my diary goes, I go with it!" But luckily Daddy didn't answer.

There is no object in recounting all the conversations that I can still remember; so much was said. I comforted Mrs. Van Daan, who was very scared. We talked about escaping and being questioned by the Gestapo, about ringing up, and being brave.

"We must behave like soldiers, Mrs. Van Daan. If all is up now, then let's go for Queen and Country, for freedom, truth, and the right, as they always say on the Dutch News from England. The only thing that is really rotten is that we get a lot of other people into trouble too. . . ."

---

[1] N.S.B.-ers: The Dutch National Socialist Movement.

Four o'clock, five o'clock, half past five. Then I went and sat with Peter by his window and listened, so close together that we could feel each other's bodies quivering; we spoke a word or two now and then, and listened attentively. In the room next door they took down the blackout. They wanted to call up Koophuis at seven o'clock and get him to send some-one around. Then they wrote down everything they wanted to tell Koophuis over the phone. The risk that the police on guard at the door, or in the warehouse, might hear the telephone was very great, but the danger of the police returning was even greater.

The points were these:

Burglars broken in: police have been in the house, as far as the swinging cupboard, but no further.

Burglars apparently disturbed, forced open the door in the warehouse and escaped through the garden.

Main entrance bolted, Kraler must have used the second door when he left. The typewriters and adding machine are safe in the black case in the private office.

Try to warn Henk and fetch the key from Elli, then go and look around the office—on the pretext of feeding the cat.

Everything went according to plan. Koophuis was phoned, the typewriters which we had upstairs were put in the case. Then we sat around the table again and waited for Henk or the police.

Peter had fallen asleep and Van Daan and I were lying on the floor, when we heard loud footsteps downstairs. I got up quietly: "That's Henk."

"No, no, it's the police," some of the others said.

Someone knocked at the door, Miep whistled. This was too much for Mrs. Van Daan, she turned as white as a sheet and sank limply into a chair; had the tension lasted one minute longer she would have fainted.

Our room was a perfect picture when Miep and Henk entered, the table alone would have been worth photographing! A copy of *Cinema and Theater*, covered with gum and a remedy for diarrhea, opened at a page of dancing girls, two jam pots, two started loaves of bread, a mirror, comb, matches, ash, cigarettes, tobacco, ash tray, books, a pair of pants, a torch, toilet paper, etc., etc., lay jumbled together in variegated splendor.

Of course Henk and Miep were greeted with shouts and tears. Hank mended the hole in the door with some planks, and soon went off again to inform the police of the burglary. Miep had also found a letter under the warehouse door from the night watchman Slagter, who had noticed the hole and warned the police, whom he would also visit.

So we had half an hour to tidy ourselves. I've never seen such a change take place in half an hour. Margot and I took the bedclothes downstairs, went to the W.C., washed, and did our teeth and hair. After that I tidied the room a bit and went upstairs again. The table there was already cleared, so we ran off some water and made coffee and tea, boiled the milk, and laid the table for lunch. Daddy and Peter emptied the potties and cleaned them with warm water and chlorine.

At eleven o'clock we sat round the table with Henk, who was back by that time, and slowly things began to be more normal and cozy again. Henk's story was as follows:

Mr. Slagter was asleep, but his wife told Henk that her husband had found the hole in our door when he was doing his tour round the canals, and that he had called a policeman, who had gone through the building with him. He would be coming to see Kraler on Tuesday and would tell him more then. At the police station they knew nothing of the burglary yet, but the policeman had made a note of it at once and would come and look round on Tuesday. On the way back Henk happened to meet our greengrocer at the corner, and told him that the house had been broken into. "I know that," he said quite coolly. "I was passing last evening with my wife and saw the hole in the door. My wife wanted to walk on, but I just had a look in with my torch; then the thieves cleared at once. To be on the safe side, I didn't ring up the police, as with you I didn't think it was the thing to do. I don't know anything, but I guess a lot."

Henk thanked him and went on. The man obviously guesses that we're here, because he always brings the potatoes during the lunch hour. Such a nice man!

It was one by the time Henk had gone and we'd finished doing the dishes. We all went for a sleep. I awoke at a quarter to three and saw that Mr. Dussel had already disappeared. Quite by chance, and with my sleepy eyes, I ran into Peter in the bathroom; he had just come down. We arranged to meet downstairs.

I tidied myself and went down. "Do you still dare to go to the front attic?" he asked. I nodded, fetched my pillow, and we went up to the attic. It was glorious weather, and soon the sirens were wailing; we stayed where we were. Peter put his arm around my shoulder, and I put mine around his and so we remained, our arms around each other, quietly waiting until Margot came to fetch us for coffee at four o'clock.

We finished our bread, drank lemonade and joked (we were able to again), otherwise everything went normally. In the evening I thanked Peter because he was the bravest of us all.

None of us has ever been in such danger as that night. God truly protected us; just think of it—the police at our secret cupboard, the light on right in front of it, and still we remained undiscovered.

If the invasion comes, and bombs with it, then it is each man for himself, but in this case the fear was also for our good, innocent protectors. "We are saved, go on saving us!" That is all we can say.

This affair has brought quite a number of changes with it. Mr. Dussel no longer sits downstairs in Kraler's office in the evenings, but in the bathroom instead. Peter goes round the house for a checkup at half past eight and half past nine. Peter isn't allowed to have his window open at nights any more. No one is allowed to pull the plug after half past nine. This evening there's a carpenter coming to make the warehouse doors even stronger.

Now there are debates going on all the time in the "Secret Annexe." Kraler reproached us for our carelessness. Henk, too, said that in a case like that we must never go downstairs. We had been pointedly reminded that we are in hiding, that we are Jews in chains, chained to one spot, without any rights, but with a thousand duties. We Jews mustn't show our feelings, must be brave and strong, must accept all inconveniences and not grumble, must do what is within our power and trust in God. Sometime this terrible war will be over. Surely the time will come when we are people again, and not just Jews.

Who had inflicted this upon us? Who has made us Jews different from all other people? Who has allowed us to suffer so terribly up till now? It is God that has made us as we are, but it will be God, too, who will raise us up again. If we bear all this suffering and if there are still Jews left, when it is over, then Jews, instead of being doomed, will be held up as an example. Who knows, it might even be our religion from which the world and all peoples learn good, and for that reason and that reason only do we have to suffer now. We can never become just Netherlanders, or just English, or representatives of any country for that matter, we will always remain Jews, but we want to, too.

Be brave! Let us remain aware of our task and not grumble, a solution will come, God has never deserted our people. Right through the ages there have been Jews, through all the ages they have had to suffer, but it has made them strong too; the weak fall, but the strong will remain and never go under!

During that night I really felt that I had to die, I waited for the police, I was prepared, as the soldier is on the battlefield. I was eager to lay down my life for the country, but now, now I've been saved again, now my first wish after the war is that I may become Dutch! I love the Dutch, I love this country, I love the language and want to work here. And even if I have to write to the Queen myself, I will not give up until I have reached my goal.

I am becoming still more independent of my parents, young as I am, I face life with more courage than Mummy; my feeling for justice is immovable, and truer than hers. I know what I want, I have a goal, an opinion, I have a religion and love.

Let me be myself and then I am satisfied. I know that I'm a woman, a woman with inward strength and plenty of courage.

If God lets me live, I shall attain more than Mummy ever had done, I shall not remain insignificant, I shall work in the world and for mankind!

And now I know that first and foremost I shall require courage and cheerfulness!

Yours, Anne

Saturday, 15 July, 1944

Dear Kitty,

We have had a book from the library with the challenging title of: *What Do You Think of the Modern Young Girl?* I want to talk about this subject today.

The author of this book criticizes "the youth of today" from top to toe, without, however, condemning the whole of the young brigade as "incapable of anything good." On the contrary, she is rather of the opinion that if young people wished, they have it in their hands to make a bigger, more beautiful and better world, but that they occupy themselves with superficial things, without giving a thought to real beauty.

In some passages, the writer gave me very much the feeling she was directing her criticism at me, and that's why I want to lay myself completely bare to you for once and defend myself against this attack.

I have one outstanding trait in my character, which must strike anyone who knows me for any length of time, and that is my knowledge of myself. I can watch myself and my actions, just like an outsider. The Anne of every day I can face entirely without prejudice, without making excuses for her and watch what's good and what's bad about her. This "self-consciousness" haunts me, and every time I open my mouth I know as soon as I've spoken whether "that ought to have been different" or "that was right as it was." There are so many things about myself that I condemn; I couldn't begin to name them all. I understand more and more how true Daddy's words were when he said: "All children must look after their own upbringing." Parents can only give good advice or put them on the right paths, but the final forming of a person's character lies in their own hands.

In addition to this, I have lots of courage, I always feel so free and so young! I was glad when I first realized it, because I don't think I shall easily bow down before the blows that inevitably come to everyone.

But I've talked about these things so often before. Now I want to come to the chapter of "Daddy and Mummy don't understand me." Daddy and Mummy have always thoroughly spoiled me, were sweet to me, defended me, and have done all that parents could do. And yet I've felt so terribly lonely for a long time, so left out, neglected, and misunderstood. Daddy tried all he could to check my rebellious spirit, but it was no use, I have cured myself, by seeing for myself what was wrong in my behavior and keeping it before my eyes.

How is it that Daddy was never any support to me in my struggle, why did he completely miss the mark when he wanted to offer me a helping hand? Daddy tried the wrong methods, he always talked to me as a child who was going through difficult phases. It sounds crazy, because Daddy's the only one who has always taken me into his confidence, and no one but Daddy has given me the feeling that I'm sensible. But there's one thing he's omitted: you see, he hasn't realized that for me the fight to get on top was more important than all else. I didn't want to hear about "symptoms of your age," or "other girls," or "it wears off by itself"; I didn't want to be treated as a girl-like-all-others, but as Anne-on-her-own merits. Pim didn't understand that. For that matter, I can't confide in anyone, unless they tell me a lot about themselves, and as I know very little about Pim, I don't feel that I can tread upon more intimate ground with him. Pim always takes up the older, fatherly attitude, tells me that he too has had similar passing tendencies. But still he's not able to feel with me like a friend, however hard he tries. These things have made me never mention my views on life nor my well-considered theories to anyone but my diary and, occasionally, to Margot, I concealed from Daddy everything that perturbed me; I never shared my ideals with him. I was aware of the fact that I was pushing him away from me.

I couldn't do anything else. I have acted entirely according to my feelings, but I have acted in the way that was best for my peace of mind. Because I should completely lose my repose and self-confidence, which I have built up so shakily, if, at this stage, I were to accept criticisms of my half-completed task. And I can't do that even from Pim, although it sounds very hard, for not only have I not shared my secret thoughts with Pim but I have often pushed him even further from me, by my irritability.

This is a point that I think a lot about: why is it that Pim annoys me? So much so that I can hardly bear him teaching me, that his affectionate ways strike me as being put on, that I want to be left in peace and would really prefer it if he dropped me a bit, until I felt more certain in my attitude towards him. Because I still have a gnawing feeling of guilt over that horrible letter that I dared to write him when I was so wound up. Oh, how hard it is to be really strong and brave in every way!

Yet this was not my greatest disappointment; no, I ponder far more over Peter than Daddy. I know very well that I conquered him instead of he conquering me. I created an image of him in my mind, pictured him as a quiet, sensitive, lovable boy, who needed affection and friendship. I needed a living person to whom I could pour out my heart; I wanted a friend who'd help to put me on the right road. I achieved what I wanted, and slowly but surely, I drew him towards me. Finally, when I had made him feel friendly, it automatically developed into an intimacy which, on second thought, I don't think I ought to have allowed. . . .

"For in its innermost depths youth is lonelier than old age." I read this saying in some book and I've always remembered it, and found it to be true. Is it true then that grownups have a more difficult time here than we do? No, I know it isn't. Older people have formed their opinions about everything, and don't waver before they act. It's twice as hard for us young ones to hold our ground, and maintain our opinions, in a time when all ideals are being shattered and destroyed, when people are showing their worst side, and do not know whether to believe in truth and right and God.

Anyone who claims that the older ones have a more difficult time here certainly doesn't realize to what extent our problems weigh down on us, problems for which we are probably much too young, but which thrust themselves upon us continually, until, after a long time, we think we've found a solution, but the solution doesn't seem able to resist the facts which reduce it to nothing again. That's the difficulty in these times: ideals, dreams, and cherished hopes rise within us, only to meet the horrible truth and be shattered.

It's really a wonder that I haven't dropped all my ideals, because they seem so absurd and impossible to carry out. Yet I keep them, because in spite of everything I still believe that people are really good at heart. I simply can't build up my hopes on a foundation consisting of confusion, misery, and death. I see the world gradually being turned into a wilderness, I hear the ever approaching thunder, which will destroy us too, I can feel the sufferings of millions and yet, if I look up into the heavens, I think that it will all come right, that this cruelty too will end, and that peace and tranquillity will return again.

In the meantime, I must uphold my ideals, for perhaps the time will come when I shall be able to carry them out.

Yours, Anne

Discussion

1. After the burglary Anne wrote in her diary: "I shall not remain insignificant, I shall work in the world and for mankind! And now I know that first and foremost I shall require courage and cheerfulness!" Why would it require courage and cheerfulness to "work in the world and for mankind"?

2. What do you learn about Anne from the things she says in her diary?

3. It has been over forty years since Anne died in a concentration camp. Why do you think her diary continues to have such an impact on people around the world?

Epilogue

Anne Frank and the others in the attic in Amsterdam were captured on August 4, 1944. They were sent to a concentration camp in Holland. Later, they made the long journey to Auschwitz, the notorious camp in Poland where four million Jews died in the gas chambers.

Mrs. Frank, who gradually lost her mind, died in January, 1945. Margot and Anne were sent to the camp Bergen-Belsen in Germany, where they died of typhus three weeks before British troops liberated the camp. It is believed that Mrs. Van Daan also died during the typhus epidemic. Mr. Van Daan died in the gas chambers at Auschwitz. Peter was among the prisoners taken from Auschwitz by the Nazis as they fled the Russian invasion. He was not heard of again. Mr. Dussel died in another camp in Germany.

Roundtable Discussion

1. It has been said that those who do not remember history are condemned to repeat it. What does this mean? Do you agree? What can society do to see that Anne's story does not happen again?

2. Although they were in hiding, Anne, her family, and their friends were aware of the atrocities being inflicted upon the Jews. Yet Anne writes in her diary: ". . . in spite of everything I still believe that people are really good at heart." Do you agree? Explain your answer.

3. When asked how he knew the human race was worth saving, a United States Supreme Court Justice answered, "I have read Anne Frank's diary." What do you think he meant?

I Dream a World

I dream a world where man
No other will scorn,
Where love will bless the earth
And peace its paths adorn.
I dream a world where all
Will know sweet freedom's way,
Where greed no longer saps the soul
Nor avarice blights our day.
A world I dream where black or white,
Whatever race you be,
Will share the bounties of the earth
And every man is free,
Where wretchedness will hang its head,
And joy, like a pearl,
Attend the needs of all mankind.
Of such I dream—
Our world!

Langston Hughes

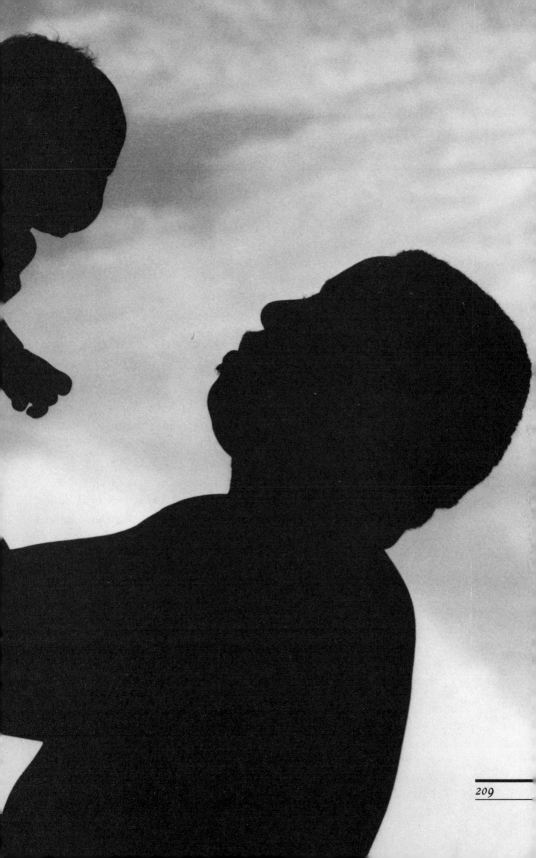

About the Authors

Frances Goodrich Born in New Jersey in 1890, Frances Goodrich became interested in dramatics while a student at Vassar College. After graduating from college, she became a successful actress in New York City. There she met Albert Hackett in 1924. Eight years later, they were married. Together they began to write plays and film scripts. In two years they wrote eight different versions of the play they eventually called *The Diary of Anne Frank*. Now world-famous, the play won a Pulitzer Prize, a Tony Award, and the New York Drama Critics' Circle Award.

Albert Hackett Hackett's parents were professional actors, and young Albert made his first stage appearance when he was six. He was born in New York City in 1900. After his marriage in 1932 to Frances Goodrich, the couple moved to Hollywood to work on film scripts. The Hacketts once explained that they wrote in a room at separate desks facing in opposite directions. Then they would exchange what they had written, criticize each other's work, and then rewrite. *The Diary of Anne Frank* is the most famous of the plays they produced in this manner.

Anne Frank Anne Frank was born in Frankfurt, Germany, in 1929. She and her family moved to the Netherlands in 1933 when the Germans began the persecution of Jews. When the Nazis occupied the Netherlands, Anne and her family hid for two years in the secret attic of an Amsterdam office building. During that time, Anne kept a diary. Following Anne's death in a concentration camp her father published her diary. It has had a tremendous impact on the world. Anne's original diary can be found in the Jewish Historical Museum, which opened in Amsterdam in May, 1987.

Langston Hughes Langston Hughes is one of the most well-known black writers of the twentieth century. He was born in Missouri in 1902. Educated at Columbia University, he became a poet, novelist, short story writer, song lyricist, playwright, radio writer, and author of juvenile books. Hughes lived in many parts of the world, including Mexico, France, Italy, and Spain. It was Hughes's belief that "most people are generally good, in every race and in every country." He used this theme in many of his stories, plays, and poems. His collections of poetry include *The Weary Blues,* which won several awards. Hughes died in New York in 1967.

Glossary

al·be·it (ôl bē′ ĭt) *conj.* Although; even though; *They proposed an imaginative, albeit impractical, idea.*

an·i·ma·tion (ăn′ ə mā′ shən) *n.* The condition or quality of being alive; liveliness; vitality.

an·tic·i·pate (ăn tĭs′ ə pāt′) *v.* **1.** To foresee, expect, or consider in advance. **2.** To deal with in advance: *He doesn't run into trouble because he anticipates problems.*

at·tain (ə tān′) *v.* **1.** To gain, accomplish, or achieve by effort. **2.** To arrive at or reach through time, growth, or movement.

bri·gade (brĭ gād′) *n.* **1.** A large army unit. **2.** Any large group.

car·il·lon (kăr′ ə lŏn′) *or* (-lən′) *n.* A set of bells hung in a tower and played from a keyboard.

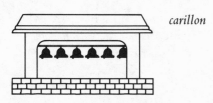

carillon

choice (chois) *adj.* Of fine quality; very good; select: *The corner market offers only choice meats and vegetables.*

co·ed·u·ca·tion·al (kō′ĕj ŏŏ kā′ shə nəl) *adj.* Of or pertaining to the system in which boys and girls attend the same school and the same classes.

co·gnac (kōn′ yăk) *or* (kŏn′-) *n.* A fine brandy originally made in the region of Cognac, a town in western France.

con·vul·sive (kən vŭl′ sĭv) *adj.* Of or like convulsions—violent, involuntary muscular contractions: *He broke into convulsive sobs after he heard the terrible news.*

di·van (dĭ văn′) *or* (dī′ văn′) *n.* A long couch, usually without a back or arms.

divan

en·hance (ĕn hăns′) *v.* To add to; make greater; increase, as in value, cost, or beauty: *The new garden will enhance the beauty of his house.*

fa·tal·ist (fāt′ l ĭst) *n.* A person who believes that all events are determined in advance by fate and cannot be altered by man.

ă pat / ā pay / â care / ä father / ĕ pet / ē be / ĭ pit / ī pie / î fierce / ŏ pot / ō go / ô paw, for / oi oil / ŏŏ book / ōō boot / ou out / ŭ cut / û fur / th the / th thin / hw which / zh vision / ə ago, item, pencil, atom, circus

for·lorn (fôr **lôrn′**) *adj*. **1.** Deserted; forsaken; abandoned. **2.** Wretched or pitiful in appearance or condition: *The forlorn stray dog was shaking from the cold.*

fran·tic (**frăn′** tĭk) *adj*. Very excited with fear or anxiety; desperate; frenzied: *The thief was frantic at the thought of being caught.*

fren·zy (**frĕn′** zē) *n*. Wild excitement or a display of emotion suggesting madness, often accompanied by vigorous activity: *The sharks had gone mad and were dashing about in a blind frenzy.*

gaunt·let (**gônt′** lĭt) *or* (**gănt′**-) *n*. **1.** An old form of punishment in which a person was forced to run between two lines of men who struck him with clubs, sticks, or other weapons. **2.** A severe test, criticism; an ordeal: *The candidate had to run the gauntlet of questions from the press.*

gnaw·ing (**nô′** ĭng) *adj*. **1.** Biting or chewing with the teeth. **2.** Troubling or distressing: *The spy had a gnawing fear of being discovered.*

in·dig·na·tion (ĭn′ dĭg **nā′** shən) *n*. Anger aroused by something unjust or mean.

in·suf·fer·a·ble (ĭn **sŭf′** ər ə bəl) *adj*. Not capable of being endured; intolerable: *I find people who talk a lot insufferable.*

in·ter·lude (**ĭn′** tər lōōd′) *n*. Something, such as an event, episode, or period of time, that intervenes or interrupts the course of events: *There was a brief interlude between the scheduled meetings.*

in·ti·mate (**ĭn′** tə mĭt) *adj*. **1.** Marked by a close and thorough acquaintance. **2.** Very personal; close: *The two women have been intimate friends for years.*

in·tu·i·tion (ĭn tōō **ĭsh′** ən) *or* (–tyōō–) *n*. **1.** The power of knowing or understanding something instantly, by instinct, without having to reason it out or get proof. **2.** A perception based on insight or instinct: *Her intuition told her to avoid the sensitive subject.*

ir·ri·ta·bil·i·ty (ĭr′ ĭ tə **bĭl′** ə tē) *n*. Annoyance, anger, or exasperation; ill temper: *His irritability was caused by lack of sleep.*

loathe (lō*th*) *v*. To regard with intense dislike; detest: *I loathe celery and never eat it.*

make·shift (**māk′** shĭft′) *adj*. Serving as a temporary substitute: *We used a makeshift shelter until a permanent one was built.*

ă pat / ā pay / â care / ä father / ĕ pet / ē be / ĭ pit / ī pie / î fierce / ŏ pot / ō go / ô **paw, for** / oi **oil** / ŏŏ **book** / ōō **boot** / ou **out** / ŭ **cut** / û **fur** / *th* **the** / th **thin** / hw **which** / zh **vision** / ə **ago, item, pencil, atom, circus**

mer·cu·ri·al (mər **kyŏor'** ē əl) *adj.*
1. Clever, shrewd, and quick, like the Roman god Mercury. 2. Changeable; fickle: *Her mercurial moods are very hard to predict.*

me·tic·u·lous (mə **tĭk'** yə ləs) *adj.* Very careful and precise: *The diligent clerk kept meticulous records.*

ob·li·ga·tion (ŏb' lĭ **gā'** shən) *n.* A legal, social, or moral requirement, duty, or promise that has the power of binding one to a certain action: *As captain of the team, I have an obligation to be present at all practices.*

os·ten·ta·tious (ŏs' tĕn **tā'** shəs) *or* (–tən–) *adj.* Elaborately showy so as to impress others: *Her ostentatious gown looked peculiar at the simple dinner.* —**os·ten·ta'tious·ly** *adv.*

pan·de·mo·ni·um (păn' də **mō'** nē əm) *n.* Wild confusion and noise; uproar: *Pandemonium followed the home team's victory.*

per·turb (pər **tûrb'**) *v.* To make uneasy or anxious; disturb; upset: *His friend's foolish behavior perturbed him.*

po·grom (pə **grŭm'**) *or* (–**grŏm**) *or* (**pō'** grəm) *n.* An organized and often officially approved massacre or persecution of a minority group.

poise (poiz) *n.* 1. Balance; stability. 2. Sureness and dignity of manner; composure: *Cathy's nervousness about performing shattered her usual poise.*

pon·der (**pŏn'** dər) *v.* To think or consider carefully and at length: *The judge pondered the situation before announcing a decision.*

re·bel·lious (rĭ **bĕl'** yəs) *adj.* 1. In open revolt against a government or ruling authority. 2. Marked by or showing open resistance to established authority. 3. Not manageable; unruly.

re·morse (rĭ **môrs'**) *n.* Bitter regret or guilt for having done something harmful, wrong, or unjust: *The child was stricken with remorse after picking the neighbor's flowers.*

re·proach·ful (rĭ **prŏch'** fəl) *adj.* Expressing blame or disapproval: *My mother gave me a reproachful glance when she found the cookies missing.* —**re·proach'ful·ly** *adv.*

rig·id (**rĭj'** ĭd) *adj.* Not changing shape or bending; stiff; inflexible.

satch·el (**săch'** əl) *n.* A small bag or piece of hand luggage, often having a shoulder strap, used to carry items such as books or clothes.

satchel

set·tee (sĕ **tē'**) *n.* A small sofa with a back and arms.

stealth·y (**stĕl'** thē) *adj.* Quiet so as to avoid notice; sneaky: *She broke into a stealthy walk as she neared the forbidden room.* —**stealth'i·ly** *adv.*

stole (stōl) *n.* **1.** A long, narrow scarf, usually of embroidered silk or linen, worn by clergymen. **2.** A long scarf of cloth or fur worn around a woman's shoulders.

stole

stu·di·ous (stoo′ dē əs) *or* (styoo′–) *adj.* **1.** Devoted to study. **2.** Earnest; purposeful; diligent: *It will take studious effort to finish the job on time.* —**stu′di·ous·ly** *adv.*

su·per·fi·cial (soo′ pər f ĭsh′ əl) *adj.* **1.** Of, on, near, or affecting the surface. **2.** Concerned only with what is apparent or obvious; shallow: *He is a superficial person, caring only about money.*

var·i·e·gat·ed (vâr′ ē ĭ gā′ tĭd) *adj.* **1.** Having streaks, marks, or patches of different colors. **2.** Distinguished or characterized by variety: *The huge museum displays a variegated collection of objects.*

ă pat / ā pay / â care / ä father / ĕ pet / ē be / ĭ pit / ī p ie / î fierce / ŏ pot / ō go / ô paw, for / oi oil / ŏŏ book / ōō boot / ou out / ŭ cut / û fur / *th* the / th thin / hw which / zh vision / ə ago, item, pencil, atom, circus